PRAISE FOR CRYSTALIZE YOUR HEALTH

If you are determined to not only survive but thrive beyond a difficult medical diagnosis, *Crystalize Your Health* is the inspirational guidebook you crave. Packed with actionable advice from fellow thrivers, many of them experts in their own right, this book will help you reclaim & restore your natural vitality on every level, regardless of the health challenges you face.

— ADRIENNE MACIAIN, PH.D., BEST-SELLING
AUTHOR OF *SPARK GENIUS: CREATIVE FLOW
UNLEASHED*

For those struggling with chronic illness, this book provides a deep understanding of self-discovery and healing. It is an eye opener for anyone who has faced hardships in life that have hurt so deeply that they've triggered disease. The stories of different women suffering in a similar way and overcoming their fears is highly encouraging for anyone going through a similar ordeal, to forgive and accept herself. The use of beautiful stones to heal and become stronger is full of mystery and spiritual energy. If you are ready to embark on a path of self-discovery, forgiveness, and healing, this book should be at the top of your must-read list.

— AAMIRAH NYAZEE, LUPUS SURVIVOR,
WRITER, TRAINER, & CEO OF RED MOON
COMMUNICATIONS

This gem of a book refracts light upon essential healing aspects of body, mind, emotions, and spirit.

I love how this book brilliantly weaves together intuitive crystal energies with guidance and personal narrative for transforming chronic illness into chronic wellness. To wonderfully assist in healing a wide range of chronic health concerns, there are guided instructions and personal examples for applying the author's four alchemical pillars of self-care which are truly helpful on a personal healing journey.

I sense a deep yet accessible wisdom in this book. I can personally testify to pairing the relationship of crystal gemstones with the cancer process. I have clairvoyantly seen crystal imagery in my subtle energy work with clients with cancer and an emphasis on chronic health.

If you are seeking guidance on your journey from illness to wellness, this book is a beautiful guide.

— MAYA AMAELE LIEBERMANN SUBTLE
ENERGY LIGHT WORKER & CRANIOSACRAL
THERAPY PRACTITIONER AUTHOR OF
PLANTING THE SEED

Crystalize Your Health is a powerful and inspiring memoir that takes readers on a journey of emotional healing and physical transformation. From the author's early childhood tragedies to her breast cancer diagnosis, this book is a testament to the resilience of the human spirit and the power of self-care. Through therapy, coaching, and self-help, the author has learned to nourish her emotions in a healthy way, balance them, and cultivate emotional alchemy. With a three-pillar emotional healing paradigm of Nourishment, Movement, and Emotional Alchemy, this book is a must-read for anyone who is seeking to transform their emotional and physical health. This book is a powerful reminder that through self-love, self-care, and perseverance, we can overcome any challenge and thrive.

— SONAL SINGHAL, SUSTAINABLE SUCCESS COACH OWNER AND CEO OF FLOWER POWER ACADEMY

Crystalize Your Health

Thriving Through Chronic Illness

C. D. Grenier

CRYSTALIZE YOUR HEALTH

THRIVING THROUGH CHRONIC ILLNESS

C.D. GRENIER

Red Thread Publishing LLC. 2023

Write to **info@redthreadbooks.com** if you are interested in publishing with Red Thread Publishing. Learn more about publications or foreign rights acquisitions of our catalog of books: www.redthreadbooks.com

Paperback ISBN: 978-1-955683-54-8

Ebook ISBN: 978-1-955683-53-1

Cover Art: Tarn Ellis @tarnellisart

CONTENTS

Introduction   xiii

PART I
Crystalizing Me   1

1. Alchemizing My Health   3
2. Gems of Well-Being   5
3. Curious about Crystals   10

PART II
Crystalizing Stories   13

4. Heart-Felt Connections   15

PART III
Crystalizing Nourishment   19

5. Compassionate Curiosity   21
6. Laughter   26
7. Connections   30
8. Nutrition   35
9. Nourishment Awareness   39
10. Crystal Healing Activities   41

PART IV
Crystalizing Movement   45

11. Flowing Forgiveness   47
12. Accountability   51
13. Conduit   56
14. Tapping   60
15. Resilience   64
16. Movement Awareness   69
17. Crystal Healing Movement   70

PART V
Crystalizing Emotional Alchemy   71

18. Self-Love   73
19. Spoken   78
20. Balance   84
21. Transform   90
22. Emotional Alchemy Awareness   95
23. Crystal Healing Meditation   97
24. Conclusion   99

Thanks So Much!   101
About the Author   103
Also By Crystal D. Grenier   105
Red Thread Books   107
Sources   109
Notes   113

DEDICATION

To my hubs, Marty & my girls, Baylee & Anaka
AND to all of us who are chronically fabulous
before, during, and after.

INTRODUCTION

As a breast cancer survivor, I want to support holistic health and healing through my personal perspective and transformational interviews with others thriving within a range of chronic illness. I wrote this book for women who share these circumstances to emphasize the importance around my three healing pillars of nourishment, movement, and emotional alchemy.

As women, we are taught to avoid emotion as a sign of weakness, pushing us to find other outlets of release or comfort. Or we unknowingly step into a masculine role, seeking to stroke our ego and feed all its external limbs of success. Or we willingly feel the need to care for others, taking on the maternal role expected of us without any healthy attention to ourselves. This neglect feeds negative emotion, eventually spiraling downward into disease.

Through my personal story, and those of others, my hope is for the female reader to feel a heart-felt connection with awareness and availability around healthy healing options to feel better and sustain vitality.

- Crystal D. Grenier

PART I
CRYSTALIZING ME

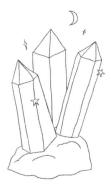

I will never be the same ME. Nor do I want to BE.

PART II

CRYSTALLIZING ME

ALCHEMIZING MY HEALTH

From my emotional birth of forced pull into this world, my childhood continued to unfold with tragedy and heartbreak. I lost my young father two days after my 2ⁿᵈ birthday, a tragic precursor into years of unhealthy stepfamily drama. The years of growing up in this environment silenced me, compounded my unprocessed grief, and had me secretly craving the physical and emotional paternal love, affection, and guidance. Another tragic loss happened in 1986 when I lost my half-sister at 17 in a car accident. This event continued to fuel my already unstable home front and pushed me further into a place of external control, emotionless, cultivating my high achieving, conflict-avoidant, type-A personality.

These tragedies and tumultuous upbringing helped silently stuff my emotions deeper into my body and mind, birthing negativity, self-deprecation, less self-love, while I waited impatiently for more affection, praise, and some type of tangible acknowledgement of acceptance. A negative emotional nourishment leading me to absorb and get lost in all the external chaos of sports, academics, other social circles, and my close friends' families.

My unhealthy emotional acceleration continued into my young adult life, compounding the already-cluttered lifestyle that I had created. Unbeknownst to me, my years of internal struggle with unnourished emotions was slowly manifesting into disease.

As an avid health and fitness guru, personally and professionally, a breast cancer diagnosis came as a complete shock. Moving through all my familiar emotions of disbelief, despair, sadness, then anger prompted me to step into my usual role of control, to take action to rid my body of disease so I could then dive deeper into my health and continue healing.

Reading books, reaching out to holistic leaders, listening to podcasts, and joining similar communities brought a variety of choices to ponder. Then it was time for me to decide how I wanted to move forward in my healing journey.

My pursuit led to an awakening awareness to implement even better food choices (plant-based & vegan); continue physical movement without an air of competition; practice mental modalities to remain calm and be present; participate socially when I feel like it; and deepen my spiritual awakening, whatever that is for me.

Through therapy, coaching, and self-help, I have learned how to nourish my emotions in a healthy way, to balance them. And this required me to investigate all my present places of well-being; physically, mentally, emotionally, socially, and spiritually. From these, I devised a three-pillar emotional healing paradigm to support my journey: Nourishment, Movement, and Emotional Alchemy. May it help you thrive as it has me!

GEMS OF WELL-BEING

All these spaces of created wellness weave into my emotional place of being. How and with what am I nourishing my body, mind, and soul? What movement modalities do I incorporate daily to stir my emotional energy to promote healing? And, how do I define my emotion, how do I wish to process it, to transform the outcome so I can stay on course to remain disease free, and live in vitality?

CONNECTION TO NOURISH. The intricate way I connect all my places of well-being fills my emotional satiety. My healthy food choices, eating for the season, herbs and spices, my presence and ambiance during my meals, my suggested supplements ... all the things I am putting into my body and how I am doing this cultivates the balance I need to stay healthy and continue healing. My daily water consumption helps me stay hydrated, and flushes my bodily system to help reduce inflammation which is a precursor to chronic illness.

NUTRITIONALLY NOURISHED. Cancer and its relation to food consumption have taken on a whole new perspective, and I have cut out foods and drinks that don't make me feel good and aren't continuing to support my healing. I have never been one to emotionally eat or starve for comfort. I eat to satisfy my hunger living consciously with plant-based, vegan food choices.

PHYSICALLY NOURISHED. Moving my body daily not only keeps the blood and fluids flowing and moving in all the right places, but more importantly, movement is essential to thriving with a chronic illness and beyond. During my treatments, movement decreased my chemo symptoms and allowed me to increase my ability to take ownership of my body and my mind. Some movement modalities that I initiate are deep breathing, chair stretching, a personal exercise routine, walking or biking in nature, dancing, yoga, and other seasonal sporting activities. I take time to slow down and live with intention which contributes to healthy movement. This behavior creates more awareness and places specific actions where and when they need to be.

MENTALLY NOURISHED. My mental health is nurtured through my awareness of presence, and is a reflection on what was learned through my experiences. With the plethora of technology, it is so easy to fall into a depressed place, lingering anxiety, and loneliness when comparing myself with others. And this place of being has led me down a path of self-loathing, self-judgment, and unworthiness.

I have found connections to nourish through music, extra sleep, meditation, self-compassion practices, and growing an optimistic attitude. Comparison really is the thief of joy, and my life is the one holding the most importance, not those of others.

EMOTIONALLY NOURISHED. I was emotionally ignorant before my breast cancer diagnosis. I lacked the awareness to feel my emotions, creating more internal intensity, suffering, and external outbursts of anger and blame. I have cultivated a healthy emotional presence to help me stay cognizant of stressors with an awareness of choices/steps to take to move through them. As I continue to groom my emotional nourishment, I confidently move towards my acute awareness of a feeling so I can own it, name it, challenge it, and change it.

SOCIALLY NOURISHED. My time alone as well as with relevant meaningful relationships provide a proportional place for me to stay happy and healthy. My social relations are easy, transparent, and effortlessly comfortable because they are nurtured through self-love and established boundaries. I have found that staying clear of draining, toxic relationships delivers a social rest and relaxation for me to sustain and maintain a healthy healing balance without the heavy feeling of guilt or regret.

SPIRITUALLY NOURISHED. I have birthed an acute awareness of deeply knowing who I am, and unconditionally love who I have become. My self-love and joy help me grow, maintain my spiritual health, and open my heart to give love more openly to others. I have noticed when I nourish my spiritual space, positive things begin to flow into my life. When confronted with conflicting people, thoughts, and things, I am more resilient and less judgmental.

EMOTIONAL MOVEMENT. Emotions creep inside bodies and minds to elicit a feeling and a reaction as either positive or negative. Feeling is the subtitle given to it as joy, fear, anger, or sadness. Attaching a definition or a thought about emotional energy offers meaning. Emotional energy is expressed through physical and mental sensations, like pain, fatigue, pressure, etc. These are signs of emotion trying to move on its own to create energy in motion.

I practice a variety of ways to move emotion out and through my body and mind. Yoga, exercise, healthy food choices, adequate water consumption, art therapy (drawing/coloring), gratitude list, mood journaling, deep breathing, Emotional Freedom Technique (EFT), and meditation to name a few.

I am still learning how to not hash and rehash a situation that evokes emotion, in my head or from my mouth. Learning to accept reason when bad feelings overwhelm me, I think of ways to make myself feel better. I try reading or watching something funny, walking or biking outside in nature, or visiting a friend or loved one.

My emotions are moving as I continue to accept self-forgiveness, practice empathy, become a better listener, cut out distractions, and stay optimistic. Without awareness of my emotional nourishment and processing, each experience or incident has me feeling one or a combination of: resentment, anger, frustration, jealousy, fatigue, lack of physical touch, sadness.

EMOTIONAL ALCHEMY. My balanced emotions put into motion with my practiced healing mechanisms have transformed my life into a disease-free living experience. I have chosen to seek out positive relationships or connections with like-minded people who share an intention of understanding. I need these people in my corner to positively impact my emotions in all spaces of well-being.

Once I process my emotions to emulate positive feelings, I now know what to do with them. I get to be inspired and empowered by my emotions through owning, naming, challenging, and changing them.

I GET TO OWN IT

All the years I harbored and packed my emotions tight, I blamed someone else, some situation, some circumstance, whatever. I have realized that these are my emotions, not someone else's. I created them and I get to choose how to use them.

I GET TO NAME IT

Calling out emotion and penning a name puts me in control and takes the power away from the emotion. This labeling brings clarity to what the emotion is, and where it is coming from. If it has a name, then I can file it away for processing, and make a mental note on how to approach it next time.

I GET TO CHALLENGE IT

As I come into power with my emotions, I find I can make choices about how I feel. If I am holding onto more than one emotion at a time, I can still challenge and make changes. I have the choice to see if there are other emotions I think would be more empowering or make the situation different. I may or may not find something else. But by challenging the emotion, I give myself the opportunity to change it.

I GET TO CHANGE IT

Emotions are choices, and I can change my mind. I can change how I want to feel about a circumstance and then take the necessary steps toward changing it. Some emotional changes will happen instantaneously in a lightbulb moment. Other emotional changes are deeper and more complex, necessitating time as well as work to sort out. Whether it takes a long time or a short time, I can recognize that the power to change my emotions belongs to ME.

Establishing a healthy emotional connection to all places of well-being through balanced nourishment, daily movement, and inspired, empowered transformation can support the many complications of chronic illness.

CURIOUS ABOUT CRYSTALS

As a young girl, I was always picking up cool-looking rocks to bring home and carefully place on my dresser, night stand, and windowsills. These treasures, in their unique form, would stand alone yet fit right in with other valuable trinkets and knick-knacks that adorned my shared bedroom.

Staying true to my minimalist way of being, and constant need for change, I would eventually purge them into house plants, art projects, or back outside to mingle among the many other rocks and gravel that made up our driveway and farmyard. New camping sites, driving adventures, and walking paths held other unique rocks and stones to gather, treasure, and find their way back home to take up the vacated spaces from those before them.

Growing up in the 60s and 70s, I loved Turquoise, Abalone, and Mother of Pearl, and gravitated to these stones in various rings and bracelets, not knowing the potential health benefits surrounding these beautiful pieces. Looking into these crystals and stones, I learned that they are believed to help a person feel compassion, love, calm, and emotional balance. Which, ironically, are the things I was subconsciously lacking throughout my childhood and, until recently, adulthood.

My interest in the beautiful colors, shapes, sizes, and types of crystals did not evolve until the last couple of years. And with the popularity and growth of spiritual and metaphysical stores, I, after careful review, delight in finding one that energetically pulls me inside to purchase a crystal(s) that resonates, in that moment, with my mood or intention.

Colorful crystals grace my office shelves, and unlike my childhood actions of rock(s) and stone(s) elimination, they will remain where they are as they are (with monthly full moon cleansing and/or rearranging). I love the study of crystals and will continue my exploration into the therapeutic attachment of health and healing.

As crystals are naturally removed from the earth, and capture the all-natural energies of the sun, moon, and oceans, they enhance our mood. Vibrating at the same pitch as humans, crystals increase our own healing potential.

Although crystals are not claimed to be medically supported, the known psychological effects of a color of a crystal realistically have benefits and associations used in therapeutic situations. Crystals can help emotional and physical healing. They are known to reduce stress, help balance emotions, bring a feeling of connection, increase the energy flow in the body, and can get rid of emotional blockages.

After feeling into the words and content of my interviews, and to keep with my passion of crystals and healing, I paired each interviewee with a crystal I felt held an association with their personal energy and their intentional message.

PART II
CRYSTALIZING STORIES

Emotional vulnerability is an invitation to ask for what you need.

HEART-FELT CONNECTIONS

I needed assurance and validation from other coaches, cancer survivors, therapists, mentors, professionals, authors, fitness experts, that what I was practicing was, in fact, the right path to be on, even though I knew in my heart, and from my past experience in health and fitness, that what I was doing during my cancer journey with nourishment, movement, and alchemy was indeed, the right place to be.

I love learning, and I am passionate about gaining relevant knowledge through educational resources to support myself and others. During my cancer experience, I dove into finding holistic practitioners, and plant-based, vegan gurus, that I could follow, to emulate their wellness practices to see if what they were offering would resonate to support my new healthy path of healing well-being.

I am not afraid to make a phone call, send an email, or drop a message to find out more about a product, person, or practice. I have an inquisitive nature, and through casual conversation, find out much more about a person than just a name and a "nice to meet you."

To expand my passion for learning, utilize my interviewing skills, gain relevant knowledge, and enhance my thoughts and actions around my current regime of healthy emotional practices, I hosted a free online Female Chronic Illness Workshop: Alchemizing Our Emotions.

My in-depth research and contacts led to fifteen heart-felt connections and shared conversations to uncover similarities and compare differences around female chronic illness.

These universal questions, with some tweaks depending on who I was interviewing, were developed to support me with not only validation but more importantly comfort and knowledge surrounding my cancer survivorship, and how I could pass on what I practice and what I learn, to help other women thrive despite having a chronic illness.

I decided that this workshop would be broken down into 3 "seasons" with each month focusing on one of my emotional healing pillars; nourishment, movement and alchemy. Each month, I featured 5 interviews on two consecutive Tuesdays.[1] Ideally, all of these speakers could have been placed under each pillar, but I needed to divide them up to accommodate the workshop layout.

The questions were simple, straightforward, and allowed for wiggle room of response. I have shared them below:

1. Please introduce yourself, share some background about YOU and your story (family dynamics, work, play...).
2. If you are like me, you remember exactly what day, time and what you were doing when you got the diagnosis of your illness. Can you please share these specifics?
3. For me, I have discovered that my emotions played a huge role in cultivating my cancer. Can you describe the most common emotional reactions when in the middle of your chronic illness?
4. When I nourish all levels of my well-being, I feel present, balanced and content. On an emotional level, how have

nutrition and/or other nourishment mechanisms played a part in your healing? Please explain.

5. I believe once we recognize our emotions, process their movement, and then utilize ways to alchemize them, we are on a healthy path towards abundant healing. How did you or do you alchemize your emotions?

<u>One more question</u>: Do you know someone who shares and/or struggles with the same illness(s) as you do? What is <u>one</u> piece of advice you can give them to move towards living their harmonious peaceful life?

Before we dive into the interviews of others, I invite you to bring out your journal or paper, and your favorite writing tool, and answer the above questions to the best of your ability.

Taking thoughts and feelings from the body and mind to express in writing or images can help move and process emotions and promote healing.

PART III
CRYSTALIZING
NOURISHMENT

It's not how you feel about the process, it's how you accept & honor
behavior change that brings real results.

COMPASSIONATE CURIOSITY

Rhodochrosite is pink-red in color, and aids healing through reducing anger; freeing up tension from anxiety; provides love and balance; encourages truth about self and others; soothes emotional stress; and supports inner strength recovery.

> "There is an importance around not having expectations about how your body should behave, instead have a compassionate curiosity for this body, and give it grace for supporting me all these years, and then ask it, 'how can I now support you as you continue to support me?' "
>
> — DR. K. EWERS, NOVEMBER 18, 2021

Dr. Keesha Ewers is an integrative medicine expert who wears several holistic healing scarves. As a popular speaker, best-selling author of three books, a retreat leader, and a hostess of a healthy Radio Network show, she began her career as a registered nurse working in intensive care. Here is her story.

Keesha: My personal journey into my chronic illness diagnosis felt like someone took the batteries out of the energizer bunny, and I was flattened with puffy joints, red and inflamed, and gained 10 extra pounds overnight. At age 30, I was diagnosed with rheumatoid arthritis (RA).

A doctor's visit moved into the history portion of the appointment to ask if anyone in my family had an autoimmune disease.

"Yeah, I think my grandfather had rheumatoid arthritis when he passed, and was in a wheelchair for a long time with it."

This admission concluded the diagnosis of RA, and the need to prescribe medication.

Being in the medical field, I questioned this result, and its side effects, and was not convinced that I had been given the short end of the genetic stick. A personal question popped into my head, *"Do I want to die, and accept the societal norm behavior surrounding autoimmune disease?"*

I found a study on yoga and autoimmune disease, and Ayurvedic medicine. The study showed a correlation between autoimmune disease and undigested anger. As a people pleaser, perfectionist, and unable to handle anger well, I started to learn meditation, and discovered my 10 year old self was sexually abused by a school principal. I wanted to die.

I dove into self-healing, eliminated my RA, and meds were not needed. This discovery led to more education and knowledge, a specialization into integrative medicine, a doctorate in sexology and a therapist role to help others.

We keep trying to separate the body and the mind, and simply medicate the body. We must look at and treat the physical, mental, and emotional as it is all connected.

I continued my life's purpose in a book to keep solving the autoimmune puzzle. As a healer with group and one-on-one trauma, I was served another blow which led to a breast cancer diagnosis at age 40.

My son confessed that he and his brother had been sexually molested by a 12 year old neighbor boy. Again, I wanted to die. The guilt around what had happened to my children while on my watch was devastating and unfathomable to comprehend. Further self-work, and a perpetrator confrontation, brought solicited forgiveness with him and my boys.

My most common emotional reaction was the shame. The deep, like deep, deep, life-sucking life-ending shame. I knew that I wanted to stick around and be there for my kids, and for their kids, so I needed to change my mind-set and forgive myself.

Once I did that, the tumor disappeared within a month of diagnosis.

We are all victims and perpetrators. I have learned from my bad decisions and screw-ups, to not judge others, or pass blame for my mistakes or illness. We all have enough work to do with ourselves, let alone worry and criticize others. We all need to deal with our own reality.

Emotionally, nutrition and/or other nourishment mechanisms played a big part in my healing.

The body is the canvas of the mind, and whatever is going on in the mind crystallizes in the body, but at the same time, what's going on in the mind often drives our food choices.

As a child and into adulthood, sugar was my comfort food. Inflammation is caused by sugar, and I was completely addicted to it when diagnosed with RA. What we consume as food plays a very big part in nourishing our body and mind plus nourishment on all levels, whether it's nourishing thoughts, vibrations, and feelings that you have for oneself, the rest of the world, and holding that space of safety.

There is an importance around not having expectations about how your body should behave, instead have a compassionate curiosity for this body, and give it grace for supporting me all these years, and then ask it, *"How can I now support you as you continue to support me?"* This question promotes an openness to create a collaborative relationship with your body rather than being in a combative one.

It's all about a different mindset. And this mindset releases a bunch of different hormones in your system, when you are filled with gratitude and appreciation for what you do have rather than angry all the time. Like you have been somehow deprived of something you want or desire.

We really do take our bodies for granted, and then when we get sick, we get pissed off at someone or something for making us sick, when it's really our fault for not paying attention to the details; checkups, healthy food choices, etc. Chronic illness is definitely a mindset adjuster.

Emotional constipation will make you sick. Our emotional digestion of thoughts and feelings are similar to the processing of food. For example, take an apple. As it moves through our digestive system to generate energy, we use what we need, and get rid of the rest and what is not necessary anymore. Toxic waste is eliminated.

To reference the apple analogy, this emotional digestion and process of elimination rid our body and mind of overload by energetically moving our emotions through journaling, deep breathing, yoga, meditation, etc., to transform them into a place of healing empowerment.

KEESHA'S WORDS OF ADVICE IN SUPPORT OF OTHERS STRUGGLING WITH ILLNESS:

Keesha: Be your own witness to self-perceptions and shift them.

I offer up a 24-hour self-observation: look at your own language, observe it.

How do you speak to yourself? Do you have a plethora of shoulds or buts? Do you speak to yourself in a judgmental way? Or are you judging others in life around you, pitting yourself as not good enough and not being whatever you expect everything to be?

LAUGHTER

A mber is a golden yellow honey color, supporting a warm, light-hearted mood; physical well-being and emotional healing; purifies negative or stuck energy; and inspires peacefulness and creates trust.

"Humor tops my chart of releases. I am always telling people, 'have you had your vitamin L today?' Laughter is the best medicine, along with love and support from family, friends, and colleagues."

— C. KORTH, DECEMBER 20, 2021

Christie Korth has fought her way to a healthy place after suffering for over ten years with various diseases and illnesses. Notably a Crohn's / Lyme disease survivor, she has authored a recipe book, and is a certified holistic health practitioner, a health counselor, and group facilitator, and is currently the director of health and wellness with American Frontline Nurses.

Her personal experiences with these diseases led to the opening of Happy and Healthy Wellness Counseling to work with others dealing with Crohn's, colitis, IBD and IBS. Her introduction and work ethic under Dr. Robert Malolo, co-founder of Brain Balance Achievement Centers, brought another opportunity to introduce and work with nutrition protocols to implement in all the center franchises.

Her mission was to harness the power of nutrition.

When interviewing Christie, her New York charm exudes throughout, and when sharing experiences, she holds nothing back.

Christie: My diagnosis of Crohn's at age 19 was embarrassing and interesting all at the same time. I had developed an anal fissure (bleeding from the rectum) and had to quietly admit this to my handsome doctor. To voice the symptom was humiliating, yet after ten years of no clear diagnosis, it was a relief to finally put a name to my illness.

My Lyme meningitis diagnosis came in 2011 while in the hospital, and upon finding out that I was pregnant with my daughter, no one wanted to treat me, and a few months later, I miscarried. This heart-wrenching experience led me to fight the battles to help others with Lyme and other infectious diseases.

Crystal: I think that illnesses surface in our bodies as a message to say, okay, wake up. It's communicating the need to change something, and this experience drives us to share our healing support with others. So that's why you and I are here doing what we're doing. So I love it. I agree 100%.

Christie shares her initial emotion about being diagnosed with her illnesses:

Christie: I was feeling lots of shock. My emotional reactions while responding to my illnesses included frustration, depression, and PTSD symptoms. When you are in the hospital 200 times in 10 years, the emotions run high and low, up and down, on a quest to figure out who you are again.

Being in the alternative place of practicing professionally and personally, frustrations would mount as others question motives in healing. A paradigm shift is happening as I and physicians are now working together to advocate the credibility around unresolved emotional trauma and chronic illness. "Our bodies keep score," (B.van der Kolk, 2014), and with my past being filled with so much trauma, I always look back and question, how is that affecting me?

Emotionally, nutrition for me, is paramount. This is huge. I'm always constantly changing my eating regime. I don't like to say the word diet because the first few letters spell die, you know what that means? Right?

We all eat differently as everybody's body is different. Your needs are going to change, as you and I both know, based upon what's going on with you at that time. Over the years, my health has changed, and whatever is happening with it, I flip up my nutrition with different things. This change up is a huge help in staying on track with my nutritional needs.

My other nourishment needs are to keep moving my body in whatever capacity that is or could be at the time. Playing the flute, drawing, painting, writing, and gardening have created many emotional outlets for me. Humor tops my chart of release. I am always telling people, "have you had your vitamin L today?" Laughter is the best medicine, along with love and support from family, friends, and colleagues.

Christie's direction of passion and work based upon what she experienced supported her transformation into positive actions to help others.

Christie: I have always wanted to be an author, and have been writing since I was a little girl. Writing was my outlet when angry or pissed off at something. And I find it cathartic to go back and reread something, to reflect on what I had been through a year or so ago, and say to myself, "Damn, you know, I just got through something that was really challenging, and then kind of reflect on how far I have come."

Another emotional organization piece is therapy energy healing. At times of defeat, throwing my hands up in the air, when I didn't want to be bothered with all this crap anymore, a big "wait a minute" would surface in my mind to ask why did this happen, and what am I doing about it? Flipping the emotional action to a positive helps people that are suffering from the same thing and in turn supports my emotional healing as well … helping just one person not be in the same place as I was.

Some words of advice to help others struggling with Lyme's or Crohn's disease include:

Christie: Encouragement is offered to share experiences, to feel through the emotions, walk through them, and not bury them, don't sweep them under a rug. When I was diagnosed with my terminal illness (Crohn's), I depicted this emotional behavior and have since found ways to alchemize my emotions. I suggest connecting to something bigger than yourself: whatever that spiritual being is for you and use it for comfort.

One more thing. Get outside in nature, soak up some sun, and just be grateful in reflecting that someone always has it worse than you do. Hang out in positivity because life is what you really make of it, and we can choose to go one way or the other. I love, "My choice is always to go to the light, not to the dark."

Realizing and living a vibrant lifestyle can be twofold. Putting that scientific metaphysical energy out there (law of attraction) along with the power of prayer can certainly generate a gratitude of healing.

CONNECTIONS

P ink Tourmaline, soft, pale pink tones, deep shades of bright reddish pink, into hot pink, guides deep mental understanding of self and situations; healing from emotional wounds; strengthens self-confidence; gives compassion; restores willingness to love, radiate love, and kindness.

"Once I started to honor and process my emotional connections, my lack of energy, states of overwhelm, my physical and food imbalances started to self-correct."

— L. MONTRY, DECEMBER 16, 2021

Lori Montry holds certifications as a Nuuaria Method Mentor and Trainer, and in the Biology of Trauma – Energy Module. She has received numerous certificates in training related to eating, psychology, trauma, somatic experiencing, and parts work. She shares her nourishment for women as an author in two collaborative books, a solo published in 2022, as a renowned speaker, a podcast host, and has a YouTube channel.

Lori: I grew up the 6th of 7 children in a familial environment lacking the attention, emotional needs, consistent attachment, and security I needed to thrive. This experience was compounded throughout with other struggles: sexual abuse, childhood, and generational traumas, with no individual time spent to nurture my needs and wants.

I sought refuge and comfort with food, and at the young age of 5, was told I needed to go on a diet as weight was becoming the more obvious issue. The advice was given to eat more fruits and veggies … without any regard to my starving internal appetite.

"Now I know what's wrong with me. Now I know why people do bad things to me. I know why I don't feel loved and secure. It's my body. Got it." I was set to fix my body and all will be right with my world. The external praise solidified my actions of eating less to lose more.

My intense struggle with food for over 3 decades created and morphed into intense body issues. A strong detour was needed to leave this lifestyle behind. Once I wrapped my head around not being a terrible willpower weakling, I started looking into my current reality with a greater understanding. This action brought a freedom to seek needed information and education and feed my curiosity around my personal issues of struggle.

My personal witness and experience of programs and self-applications forever changed me, and I gained a new perspective to create a new life for myself. This intentional process delivered a priceless value that I wanted to share with others, to help other women with their challenges creating a camaraderie that comes with having a shared experience. A gift.

Being so young, without any means or resources to handle my emotions, standing in a place of overwhelm, a lack of experience, and nowhere to run, I sought refuge in food. I always say: unexpressed emotions, they never go away, we may think we got away from them for a time, but really, they just went somewhere else. And usually what that means is, they become trapped essentially, in the body.

In all the places, emotional eating stole everything from me, my confidence, my energy, my clarity, who I was. I was still functioning, getting my degrees, raising a family, but in a robotic version of myself, as opposed to the person who shows up now.

Refusing our emotions can take a toll on our bodies and can show up in distinct, physical ways. I was inflicted with autoimmune difficulties, thyroid issues, and a long bout of hives which I attribute to living in my survival mode, an intensity of being present so I could feel the imbalance that needed correction. Once I started to honor and process my emotional connections, my lack of energy, states of overwhelm, my physical and food imbalances started to self-correct.

When in the middle of my eating struggles, I blamed myself. Everything was my fault. I am just not good enough. I would have traded places with anybody, just not to be me, because I knew they were in a better place.

I felt like I didn't deserve anything good. My perspective needed a fresh view through different lenses. To break free from the guilt and shameful past to experience intentional joy and happiness.

Dwelling on the past distracts us from where we want to go. And on the other side of this, we tell ourselves not to look back, not look at it at all. Where we end up is somewhere in the middle, glancing back to address our past in order to move forward with understanding and compassion on what's going on with me, and how I got here, and how I can support myself in the places where I need it. Those who influenced our past were most likely doing their best with their knowledge, resources and abilities and we shouldn't find fault with them. If we are not willing to look at why we need support, and how that came about, then it's difficult to provide what we really need.

When it comes to nourishment, skip the restrictions, learn how to nourish yourself. I am always in communication with what I need, stepping back to assess the situation before taking an action. Paying attention to self, what is my capability, and how can I still stay in my place of flow and ease. Keeping the head space to stay in this lane, to adjust if needed without depleting all of my energy sources.

There's such a beautiful sense of safety and care that comes from being the one that takes care of you. Taking the time to sit down and enjoy a meal is a pause to take personal action. Escaping the societal pressure to perform, to meet or exceed social and work ethic standards, and take away the need for competition. Look at how to listen better, pay more attention to self-talk and conversation with others.

I am more effective in my life and relationships. Everything I touch, when I am not pushing, lets me live in that lane of flow and ease. When we push to get more done, we are less effective at finishing.

Often, we move right into the processing of our emotions without realizing the work that needs to be done in recognizing them, and then allowing them to come through, because for so long, especially if we are used to running away from them, we are not in touch with them.

And I kind of think of it like either a friend or a relationship, right? If we've not given space to these emotions, they're not going to come forward in order for us to start to work with them. I think anger is a really great example. Because as kids, when are we ever allowed or encouraged to express and deal with our own? We get angry, and we're sent to our room and given the message, you know, especially as women, that being angry is bad. We weren't taught that anger is okay.

When we are unable to identify an emotion, how do we have an awareness of what is going on? We feel bad, but other than that, there is no information to work with.

So, creating a safe and inviting place for these emotions to come in, be heard, and be understood, questions my connection to my nervous system. Am I feeling stressed? Overwhelmed? Or am I feeling peaceful and content … when I am in this space, I can access my emotions a lot better.

Emotional processing could be to listen to what I might need. What does that feel like? Quiet time to access self, soothing music, my people support system, spend time in nature … to feel safe by being nurtured. These things allow me to have good access to my emotions.

For me, it's my pen and my journal. I could spend the whole day on my "couch of contemplation," where things are brewing, or a decision is made.

I also employ a modality called parts work, bringing in those parts of us, the part of me that's feeling angry, the part of me that's feeling, you know, the perfectionistic part of me, the rebel part of me, or whatever that part is, and bringing these different parts of me to my higher self for conversation and cooperation. Other modalities include: talking to my inner circle, color, yoga movement, and somatic practicing.

Staying emotionally nourished to move towards living your best life is all about staying connected to self. Your Higher Self, your inner wisdom, the part of you not interrupted by racing thoughts, not your emotions … it is your true essence.

This honorable connection and self-relationship create a gate for all other things to fall into place. Without this enlightenment, we are like a dog chasing our tail, uncertain of what to do next, where to go, and if what I am doing is helping. Building this foundational piece creates a strong base to operate with clarity and action.

NUTRITION

Fire Agate, a beautiful translucent deep reddish-brown base, with flashes of orange, red, green and gold color, has healing properties to sooth, calm, and balances both positive and negative energies; supports active initiative; optimistic thinking; and passionate commitment to endeavors.

"For me, it was solely about the food at first, then I began to open up to how I was feeling in my body, how I perceived my body, how I felt about the foods I was consuming."

— T. GREEN, DECEMBER 8, 2021

Tamara Green & Sarah Grossman are the founders of The Living Kitchen, a private chef company that changes people's lives through healing, nourishing food. As Sarah was unavailable for the interview, I had the pleasure of conversing with Tamara. She, as well as Sarah, are certified nutritionists, wellness chefs, TV hosts, and authors of *The Living Kitchen Cookbook.*

Tamara: We love connecting good food with health, and believe our health is often a collection of things - like, what we eat, how we eat, how we think, who we surround ourselves with and so much more. We have a strong focus on working with people with cancer, and those looking to increase their longevity and health span.

Like most of us, I grew up eating exclusively hamburgers, pizza, and chicken fingers. Along the way, I developed serious digestive issues and experienced chronic pain for nine years. This timeline of eating and then running to the bathroom became my norm, an acceptance of suffering that was concluded to be just how it is. Eventually, an irritable bowel syndrome diagnosis labeled my condition because they really didn't know what was wrong with me. My love of cooking became a platform to shift my diet as I discovered nutrition both in the kitchen and in the classroom.

My marrying of food and cooking brought to fruition the impact of a healthy well-being for self and others. My symptoms disappeared, and the motto, "Food is Medicine" became my mantra.

I now combine my knowledge of nutrition and passion for cooking to work with clients to create lasting changes in their lives. As a mom to two young boys, an importance is placed around their nutritional awareness and healthy food choices.

I am a huge proponent of the connection of emotional health to physical health. Through epigenetic study, we know that our stress can flick the switch on hormones to lead us down certain pathways. As a child, I suffered from severe anxiety (fear, new situations, teachers, etc.). This manifestation of anxiety contributed to my intense digestive pain and related issues.

Other nourishment mechanisms supporting me have developed over time, and uncovered deeper levels of awareness. For me, it was solely about the food at first, then I began to open up to how I was feeling in my body, how I perceived my body, how I felt about the foods I was consuming. My thoughts around self-image, and how I saw myself, became the core of my well-being value system.

Other focused modalities: sleep, movement, breathing & meditation to calm the anxiety beast still living inside me, required discipline to help me move mind and thoughts, and not stay stuck in old patterns or feelings. These actions, along with my dietary changes, contribute a great deal to physically feeling good and complete.

My biggest transformation is really becoming more conscious and aware of my thoughts and my feelings, and how these filter into my parenting.

I had to break generational cycles of anger which were displayed during my childhood. Becoming a parent, with instant reflexes to act as you were taught and drawn into, brought an actual emotional experience that needed more response and compassion, not a reaction. Personally, and professionally, this is a constant work in progress.

We need to realize, regardless of age, the importance of "constant evolution." Illness is bred by lack of feeling, a lack of evolving. As parents, we should be always looking at ways to improve our behaviors so our little ones, and adult ones, can emulate these behaviors in their upcoming roles.

My suggestions to those who share or struggle with a digestive illness would be to start pulling one healthy lever at a time. In looking at all your levers of well-being and healing, pick one, get focused, and allow it to work for you. We all start with a strategy, and get frustrated when it is not working fast enough, and want to bounce to something else.

Be patient, persistent, with incremental steps, and give it the space and time needed to show some results. I love starting with food personally. What can you bring in, before taking it away? Instead of cold turkey cutting the carbs and the sugar, what can you bring in to support your gut health, your hormones, your blood sugar and neurotransmitters? What is going to support that?

Putting more plants and vegetables onto your plate is a great starting point.

And remember, what works for one may not work for another. We are all made differently and crave healthy unique nutrition requirements. You can find exciting recipes and inspiring nutrition tips at www.livingkitchenwellness.com.

NOURISHMENT AWARENESS

WHAT DID I KNOW ABOUT NOURISHMENT?

Nourishment for me has always been about food. As a personal trainer and fitness instructor who has been practicing somewhat healthy eating habits for over 40 years, I rarely questioned the need to look at all places of nourishment in my place of well-being.

After having my second daughter in 2001 and working at a gym before becoming a personal trainer, I wanted to be trained to lose the post-baby weight, focus on my food intake, and experience this healthy lifestyle before I started training others to do the same. Keeping track of calories in the form of good carbs, proteins and fats was a challenge because I was not aware of what I was putting into my body without journaling it. It was truly eye-opening for me, and I did achieve my goals and moved on to train others.

Eventually, my passion waned and I was personally & professionally struggling with the lack of client commitment, and the monetary need to push supplement sales. I quit training others, and stayed in the gym as a workout junkie, and long-time fitness instructor.

WHAT DID I LEARN ABOUT NOURISHMENT?

My conversations around nourishment provided a shared perspective on how a life-changing experience causes me to look past the usual feedback or treatments to fix a health problem. I am accountable to cultivate my awareness and the choices available to help heal in whatever capacity that is for me on an individual basis.

I can look at my breast cancer diagnosis as a beautiful experience, a life-altering thing, to change my trajectory of daily living. I now look at all the places that I am nourishing myself, not only with food, as an external necessity to fuel my body, but now view the internal as perhaps more important. I need to feed my mind, my mental, my emotional, my spiritual ... healthy things, messages, images in order to obtain balance or satiety. Disease manifests and feeds off not only unhealthy eating habits, but from an accumulating internal imbalance as well.

CRYSTAL HEALING ACTIVITIES

Here are some ways you could begin to take your emotions and thoughts from your head to paper or computer. These five "actions" are carefree and flowing to get you started.

1. Three ways I could nourish myself today.
2. Three ways I could take action today.
3. Three ways I could love myself today.
4. My word of the day is...(abundance, love, forgiveness, grace, tenderness, trust, faith ...)
5. What feelings and emotions do you experience most often?

ART THERAPY

I love using art therapy, and who doesn't love to color? The crystal image in the shape of a heart is yours to fill with hues of pinks, blues, reds, yellows, purples, greens, etc.

I would suggest using colored pencils to avoid bleeding through the book page.

PART IV
CRYSTALIZING MOVEMENT

Emotional energy craves expression through physical and mental
sensations, energy in motion to promote abundant, healthy living.

FLOWING FORGIVENESS

R ose Quartz, a peaceful delicate pink color, provides lessons to self-love; brings a deep inner feeling of healing and peace; and encourages self-forgiveness and acceptance.

"For those of us struggling with breast cancer, I believe we neglect our worth, and deserving care, and we should be putting our health needs first before putting all our energy into someone else."

— T. COYOTE, NOVEMBER 2, 2021

Tara Coyote is a certified equine facilitated learning teacher, life coach, and surviving with late-stage breast cancer since 2016. Her memoir, Grace, Grit & Gratitude, A Cancer Thriver's Journey from Hospice to Full Recovery with the Healing Power of Horses, talks about overcoming adversity on so many levels, and how horses played a major role in her healing with cancer.

Tara: My life before cancer was overflowing with running a horse healing retreat center in Northern California, while holding space as a single mom to my son. I was also my best friend's 19 years main caretaker for 22 months from diagnosis to death from leukemia. This role brought much self-neglect for personal health, and once she passed, overwhelming grief. These realities revealed a painful lump discovery which needed my immediate attention.

Upon my initial diagnosis of breast cancer, I opted to follow a natural path of healing which was successful for 2.5 years. However, a stressful incident happened, and I was forced to sell my retreat center which directed a move to Hawaii.[1]

My cancer was progressively reaching stage four, hospice was recommended, I was dying. With all the grief and fear around my friend's passing, I was fearful about chemotherapy and other traditional treatments.

I faced my fear, did chemo for nine months, endured hard times, physical setbacks, but finished with remarkable results. The cancer tumors continue to shrink, but I still journey with the stage four diagnosis in my body. Scans continue to show shrinkage, my bones are growing back, and blood counts are healthy. I am grateful to be alive!

Emotions are so important to tune into unhealed trauma within yourself. Once my friend had passed, I dealt with a lot of grief, and then her diagnosis brought on more grief and fear around dying. This awareness brought much-needed emotional work, healing past childhood traumas. This process is never ending, it is a continuous path we must stay on.

Usually when there is a cancer diagnosis, the focus is on the medications and treatment protocol, which is important, but it's equally important to address the mental, the emotional component of healing. Healing emotions heals the body. Stuck emotions are stuck energy that prevents us from healing.

So that has been a big part of my mission these past six years. I continue to face the emotions that come up, release them, and get the support if I need to. And move through it, like release those emotions, emotions are meant to be felt and released.

My self-care actions to nourish my emotional health include treating myself with natural, non-toxic medicines to keep my immune system healthy. Chemotherapy does its job of eradicating the cancer cells, but it also annihilates our healthy cells too. My goal was to let chemo do its thing, but keep the immune system strong. I share on my website, www.linktr.ee/TaraCoyote and in my book, *Grace, Grit & Gratitude, a Cancer Thriver's Journey from Hospice to Full Recovery with the Healing Power of Horses*, these immune strong protocols.

Herbs, vitamins, and weekly mineral infusions are ingested to support, and on a food front, healthy eating is always key. I was conscious of what I was putting into my body: avoid sugar, eat organic and stay gluten free.

Healthy emotional intake can be difficult especially when going through rough times, so extra attention is needed to stay in the zone of processing and not relapse back into festering ways.

Taking the time to cultivate relationships and stay conscious of who you want to spend your time with is an important piece of healing as well. I held discernment in my relationships, especially those who could support my healthy ways, while discarding those toxic relationships full of constant conflict.

My horses and my other pets are my healing gift. Being around them daily and taking care of them provides a purpose of giving with unconditional love and support. As humans, our brains can be an obstacle and a hindrance to healing because we get caught up, holding onto our past stories whereas animals are living in their present. We are all blessed to share a yurt and a spanning outdoor space in beautiful Hawaii.

I allow myself time to feel my emotions. This is not always easy. So when an emotion moves inside me, I really feel it, work to release it and get it out. My horse work revolves around emotional release. They feel their emotions, act on THEM, release THEM, and go back to grazing.

Do I need to write? Do I need to scream? Do I need to reach out to a friend or a therapist? Dancing, swimming, and riding my horses are modalities I engage in to move negative energy and release emotion.

Always practice self-love & self-care. A Hawaiian friend of mine who works with plant medicine has an amazing healing story around being admitted to hospice for cancer. A coined concept, "Aloha Ma," which is called self-reflective love, which translates to mean: take care of yourself, you are worth it.

As women, we were taught to take care of others, and then focus on our needs and wants last. For those of us struggling with breast cancer, I believe we neglect our worth, and deserving care, and we should be putting our health needs first before putting all our energy into someone else.

Thank you so much. Mahalo.

When Tara and I were doing this interview, she was with her Mom in California as her health was declining. Both her parents passed within months of each other in 2022.

I shared that losing your best friend and your mom are two very different losses, but maybe going through the loss and grief of her best friend created a different path of grief and loss with her Mom.

My observation during this interview is her acquired awareness in how to take care of herself while taking care of others. A lesson learned: don't deplete yourself to fall backwards after taking so many steps forward.

Tara and I both share and convey that cancer is a message. We were meant to find it to be put on a new path of awareness around our health and emotions. Through the addressing of all things in our past, we can change the discovery of healing in our present, to live abundantly in our future.

ACCOUNTABILITY

Larimar has coloration variations from bluish white, light-blue, light-green, green-blue, turquoise blue, turquoise green, turquoise blue, offering to heal emotions with courage; to let go of self-sabotaging behavior and self victimization; bringing joy and resolve on a continued path of life; reducing stress.

"Initiation as a catalyst creates an opportunity to empower so we can shift the energy of victimhood to transmute and transform it."

— P. LAKHI, NOVEMBER 19, 2021

Priya Lakhi, is a certified master results coach, a trainer and master practitioner of neuro-linguistic programming. She has two board designation master practitioner seats in timeline therapy and hypnotherapy. She is also a magnified healing master teacher, yoga teacher, certified energy healer, and spiritual seeker.

Priya: My real story begins as an immigrant child from India. My parents and I moved to the US when I was 5 years old. My brother arrived a few years later. A shared vision of many immigrants, we were coming to the land of opportunity, all that America was and is.

This move brought a freedom filled with interesting dynamics: racism, uncomfortable situations, and employment demotions. Navigating these realities created anger and turmoil in the household with parents desperately trying to keep a roof over our heads and food on the table.

And that left very little room for emotional support. Feelings weren't talked about. My parents were brought up with disconnection around their feelings so it was hard for them to create a safe space for them. Totally unintentional. I was brought up in a house where achievement was the main value.

In our childhood, we are unaware that we are in a place that is difficult, we just know it doesn't always feel good.

This scenario is known as complex trauma. We are disconnected from our own feelings, with no safe space for them, and we feel neglected in ways that we can't talk about. Personal assumptions flood your mind about not being worthy. My role as a child is to make the grades, do the chores, excel in all that I do, and not rock the boat, all to avoid arguments in the house.

I didn't really have a crystal-clear moment in transitioning from one place to another. It was more like gradual nudges that the universe was giving me that I kept ignoring. In 2017, every single function in my life was not working well. My job as a lawyer became unfulfilling; my relationships were strained, and my finances were unsteady.

First, the universe throws a grain of sand, then a softball, then a football, and then your whole house comes falling down and you're like, oh, wait a second, what's happening? I was ignoring the signs and let my ego take over. I realized that I couldn't ignore the universe's nudges anymore, as I was not happy on all my fronts.

In the middle of my 2017 reality, I sat emotionally in a place of victimhood. This seems to be the most common starting ground for most of us: *"It is not me, it is them, if they only did something different, then I would be happy."* Everything in my life was outside of me.

My past and related circumstances are not my fault, but they are my responsibility, and I can change the outcome. Initiation as a catalyst creates an opportunity to empower so we can shift the energy of victimhood to transmute and transform it.

Interesting fact: Unlike the Western belief, other cultures view depression as a portal into something bigger. It is not labeled as good or bad, right or wrong, with a need to fix or remedy it. Suffering is needed for us to learn in all the places that we are misaligned with our perfect soul.

A cancer diagnosis or loss of job is to realize that something is not working. Unresolved trauma is at the root existing in your life, and about whether you believe you are worthy and deserving of a life you want to have. To learn the tools, we actually hold trauma in our body, without a safe space to feel the strength or energy to move it through.

There isn't really a choice, a switch to turn on and off to see sudden change. It is an awareness, an acceptance, a wholeness nourishing ourselves versus a strength towards something outside of us.

It is all about energetic prana or life force that something I am consuming has in it, the more it's going to nourish me. The more thoughtful and mindful I am of the life force in the vitality of the thing I am consuming, the easier it is for me to purify my physical body and vessel so I can have strength and mindfulness towards my own self-love, self-compassion and self-understanding.

If I am vibrating and putting foods into my system that are actually an energy of a higher vibration than I exist in the energy, it doesn't matter how much meditation, yoga, or working out I do, there will always be an imbalance. There needs to be an energetic alignment with the food that we eat.

I am grateful for my food and drink and the nourishment that they provide because we are co-creating energy that is literally making the world a better place.

Two important things to help optimize your energetic emotional movement; know your emotions, know what you are feeling. Don't numb out, know yourself. And accept your emotion where you are, allow for it because it is you.

Western culture defines emotions as good or bad and tells us we shouldn't feel or process the bad ones. Our emotions are energy in motion, and we are guided by them. An energy is rising, it is in motion, it is asking you to know it, acknowledge it, get curious about why it's there, accept it, and then the emotion should bring clarity.

Bad emotions can bring clarity too. Following the same protocol as above will take away the desire to suppress them. If they are not embraced, and are stuffed, we have no choice but to create a painful body that manifests disease.

Unfortunately, we live in a society where emotional fluidity and flexibility is not taught or accepted. This truth creates a lot of turmoil in us that leads to victimhood. So for me, the first step is always awareness. An acceptance and a knowing. Why am I feeling this way?

We are not taught to go inside, and are directed to fix the external symptom. With a traditional, holistic approach, a lot of our systems to help us navigate good well-being are not really using the tools to empower us out of victimhood. There is a teachable moment for parents on how to be more emotionally regulated so we can hold a safe space for our children.

Find joy in the work, empowerment in the work, create a community around your work. Clients want all the feel-good, but are not willing to put in the work. It is a matter of priority. Are you willing to be able to allow yourself to receive the gifts that you yourself want to give you?

Coming home to yourself is a beautiful time, and life that is easily available to anyone, anything you want is available to you, no matter how stinky that pond that you're living in might feel at this moment.

There is nothing more important to my purpose in the world than to be the best version of myself for me, and all of those I work with and love. And if no one said it, I appreciate you.

Priya's beautiful transition from the "clarity of a lawyer, to the compassion of a healer" can be found on her About Page www. awakenananda.com.

CONDUIT

Amethyst, found in various shades of purple, powerfully protects and promotes inner peace and healing, positive transformation; balance; communication; enhances intuition, spiritual growth and awareness.

"I am the bridge between knowing but not-knowing."

— T. DENDY, DECEMBER 7, 2021

Talaya Dendy was diagnosed in 2011 with Hodgkin's Lymphoma, and is now into her 11th year as a cancer thriver. Her experience and journey brought forth her current role as a cancer doula. She is the owner and CEO of "On the Other Side," www.ontheotherside.life and host of her own podcast, "Navigating Cancer Together."

Crystal: What is a cancer doula, and how does this role support others in your business?

Talaya: A doula is someone who helps another person through a major life change, or a significant health experience. And of course, cancer encompasses both places. I am essentially walking with my clients on their cancer journey, with an intense focus on the present with help to get past the challenge that is in front of them.

Prior to my cancer diagnosis, I had discovered a lump in my neck a year prior which my PA at the time blew off as a pulled muscle. My next annual with a different PA was concerned as the lump had gotten bigger and harder, and ordered the usual protocol of an ultrasound, which solidified my cancer diagnosis of Hodgkin's Lymphoma.

A nurse's phone call on a Friday afternoon knocked the breath right out of me, and she had no answers to share. Dazed and in shock, I had to wait until Monday for a referral to contact me to find out more.

When in the middle of my cancer illness, I had to become acquainted with self-compassion; gratitude for my insurance coverage to help me pay for my treatments, and the support of others. I was determined to not be hindered by cancer, and not let all the stigmas surrounding cancer cloud me with fear. I surrounded myself with joy, because the treatment was working.

Finally, one thing I did notice later, once I got through it, I was actually mourning the changes that my body was going through due to the treatments.

Prior to chemotherapy, I was able to run, jump and do all the things without getting out of breath, and then here I am, I have to put this poison into my body to save my life, but at the same time, it's killing me causing other problems.

On her relationship to nutrition:

Talaya: I had a weakness for sugar prior to my diagnosis. Studies have shown the link of sugar to cancer, and once I cut out sugar, I really felt better. I added lots of proteins to my diet, and was feeding my body those core foods that promote healing.

While I was receiving treatments, I did reach out to a social worker at the hospital, to have someone to talk to, and I felt understood. I also journaled, did meditation, and practiced mindfulness really focusing on my mind/body connection. Like you, I still went to the gym, and did what I could do. I still had to do something daily, even if it was movement around the house. I couldn't just lie there and not do anything, this to me would be giving up. Keeping normalcy as much as possible without overdoing it is a healing step forward.

I absolutely think that by being in a place of awareness with my health before I was diagnosed helped me stay active, to whatever degree that is, during and after. I also believe that being in some form of physical shape prior to starting treatment helped me get through it as well as I did.

I feel it is important to start to become active, if not already, because then if a diagnosis happens to fall into your lap and you must endure treatments, your chances of making it through with less difficulty would be somewhat easier than those who are living a very unhealthy life prior to a diagnosis.

Personally and professionally, I took my cancer experience and turned it into something that could help other people. Personally, journaling is still a huge part of my daily practice, as well as mindfulness, self-awareness, reflection, and meditation. A small support system is also important. I have three people in my circle that I trust, and can reach out to when needed.

On my website, I share four main areas of client support.

First of all, I am not a doctor with the means to diagnose. I take the information given to my clients from their doctor, and break it down so they can better understand what they are experiencing or going through. I walk them through the pros and cons so they can make their own educated decision about how they would like to proceed.

So my first area of support is around emotions/mindset which has been a common thread throughout our conversation. This place of support helps them not get stuck in that dark place where cancer likes to take us. Having that personal support group with someone who has already walked through this, answer their questions, and reassure them that what they are feeling and going through is normal.

The second area is health. This could encompass nutrition, exercise, anything related to your health.

The third is understanding their treatment options. Help them find clinical trials, and the understanding around what that means and what it entails.

The fourth is communication, and how that conversation is going with loved ones, your employer, friends, and other important relationships. When someone is diagnosed, others can shut down because they don't know what to say. There is a lot of awkwardness and confusion. I also help clients with their insurance submissions, and help them navigate the healthcare system as a whole.

I am the bridge between knowing but not-knowing.

Some parting words of advice to move towards your vitality would be to evaluate your life, and make changes to release what is no longer working, holds no value, or isn't serving you anymore.

Life is too precious to waste in a space that doesn't fill your cup.

TAPPING

Black Onyx, promotes vigor, stamina and determination; supports movement of energetic blockages, doubts and fears; opens pathways to more emotional, physical, and spiritual energy.

"Tapping feeds the reduction of stress and other upsetting emotions to deliver a peace of mind, and enhances the positive."

— B. YATES, NOVEMBER 29, 2021

Bradley Yates, an Emotional Freedom Technique (EFT) master expert, hypnotherapist, author, and presenter works with a diverse group of clients. Before this path of therapy, Brad started as an actor, traveling the world doing theater, and ending up in Hollywood to live the movie star dream. Falling in love, getting married, and with the arrival of his first child, questioned this path of profession, and he felt he needed a backup plan.

Brad: I have always been fascinated with the power of the mind. And upon hearing about a course in hypnotherapy, I felt confident in pursuing it plus I had the theater trained voice that would certainly be in my favor.

During this time, I had a small hypnotherapy office, with little clientele, and I was renting out my space to others to help promote their businesses. Being in competition with other men vying for the same type of acting roles, I felt a shift to move from my first "job" as an actor, into my backup plan as a therapist. It was and is all about the timing of things. I wasn't sad or disappointed, and was OK with this change of professional direction.

EFT or tapping, is derived from acupuncture. For many many years, Chinese medicine has proclaimed a flow of energy throughout the body along pathways called meridians. When this energy flows naturally, we experience our natural state of physical and emotional health and well-being.

When this energy gets stuck, we don't feel good, our thoughts are muddled, and our choices are not the best. Many unfortunate things can happen from this energy block.

In traditional acupuncture, the doctor would stick needles in these key points to stimulate that healthy flow of energy, and similarly, we are tapping our fingertips on these same points to get that energy moving.

Modern research continues to grow showing EFT as a profound tool for regulating our stress levels. Most of the issues we face, physically and emotionally, are caused or worsened by stress. We have certainly seen how physical ailments and chronic illnesses are manifestations of unresolved emotions. And tapping is an amazing tool for getting resolution on a lot of that emotional stuff.

Many people have found tapping beneficial with a variety of issues, including ailments and chronic illnesses. Namely, the side effects of having a chronic illness; the pain, fatigue, guilt, fear, resentment, and anger, all the emotions and feelings that just make it that much worse, that much more upsetting.

Let's see if we can resolve or relieve this with a tap. Tapping not only alleviates the pain, but lowers the emotional discomfort that accompanies the suffering.

Tapping feeds the reduction of stress and other upsetting emotions to deliver a peace of mind, and enhances the positive.

To illustrate this positivity concept, I like to refer to Michelangelo's process of art creation. The artist said that the statues are already there, perfectly inside the big slab of marble, and all I have to do is chip away what doesn't belong to reveal the masterpiece. It is the same thing we are doing with tapping, chipping away to reveal our healthiest, happiest, best self-inside! Getting rid of what doesn't belong; the guilt, the shame, the unworthiness ... all those uncomfortable feelings that get in the way.

Therefore naturally enhancing the more positive feelings, finding joy where we can, finding hope where we can. Making the most of the situation regardless of the active restrictions.

To optimize my emotions, I tap at least once a day to maintain my emotional, spiritual and physical well-being. And I recommend to others to follow this same energetic hygiene. As we practice daily physical hygiene of showering and brushing our teeth to get rid of the stink and smell, tapping cleanses out the stress that is building up in our bodies that could eventually birth symptoms and illness.

Depending on different factors, especially when working with clients, I get double doses of tapping because I am tapping on myself while they are tapping on themselves.

To help move towards living an abundant life, I would come back around to the benefits of tapping, using this practice to gain as much peace of mind as possible. And recognizing that even with the issues that we are dealing with, there are opportunities to experience more peace and joy.

We are all doing the best we can with the programming we have, the lessons we have been taught, to share the message that it is possible to find joy with tapping. Keeping an open-mind to at least try it is always an invitation.

The challenge with EFT is that people hear of the one-minute wonders of someone's pain scale going from 8 out of 10 to zero, and they compare their experience to question its validity.

We are all different, and what works for one, may not work as fast for another. It might take more time for you to feel the results.

Muscle movement to build happens through electrical impulses. Mental tapping works the same way, sending impulses and thoughts to the meridian points to bring physical and emotional benefits.

RESILIENCE

S moky Quartz, a variety of translucent and transparent brownish-gray or black crystals, helps us stay centered and driven; balances our energetic field; brings an emotional calmness, grounding, strength and power.

"Also resorting to what always makes me feel better, which is movement, lets me take control over what I can control. Feeling physically strong has always helped me emotionally."

— A. MISSIMER, DECEMBER 8, 2021

Dr. Arianne Missimer is a physical therapist, registered dietitian, yoga teacher, mindfulness educator, author and cancer survivor. Dr. Arianne is the founder of the movement paradigm, and has held a strong presence in the health field for over 22 years.

Arianne: My career started as owner of my first personal training studio at age 22, while simultaneously receiving my nutrition degree. I was passionate about helping people with a dual nutrition and fitness perspective. Four years later, my deeper interest in the body and the rehabilitative side of things took me back to school to pursue my PT degree. While keeping all these balls in the air, I had a vision of opening up a multidisciplinary practice where I could support the whole body.

At 25, a cancer diagnosis brought clarity, a deeper personal and professional desire to continue following my dream and open up my practice; an integrative health center; the movement paradigm. We focus on mindset, nutrition, and movements.

A couple of months before I got the diagnosis, I noticed a pinpoint nerve pain in my calf. My first thoughts were too much exercising or movement, which seemed logical, but after seeing an orthopedic oncologist, and a biopsy a week later, I was diagnosed with liposarcoma. A very rare form of cancer, stage 3 and very aggressive.

The call to communicate my cancer diagnosis came at a conference of continuing education, which is one of my favorite things to do, and I was at a place where I couldn't have been happier.

Treatment would need to be started right away, and I felt like my whole world was ending, fast. Time stood still as I tried to collect my thoughts to process this information. I needed to phone my fiancé (we were getting married in two months), and my mom and dad who both lost their son, my brother, to cancer at the age of 29.

As I was still attending my conference, my evening alone in my hotel room was brutal.

With my education and experience thus far, I found out that there are no genetic, environmental or lifestyle links to sarcoma. This is where the research stands as of right now. I feel my cancer came to me as a message because I was running myself ragged; running a business, being a clinic director of a PT clinic, planning a wedding, etc.

Personally, there may be a genetic predisposition to cancer as my mom had cancer, and my brother died of cancer as well. However, I do think there was a lifestyle component as this underlying low level stress that I wasn't totally aware of.

From a very young age, resilience has been one of my strong suits. Anything that came my way, I felt like I could manage it, but I never realized how much I was stuffing emotions, and for a very long time.

Going through cancer, I had done a lot of reflection, and gotten very interested in mindfulness, the polyvagal theory, and emotions. So when cancer hit me, I did exactly what I know best, which is to fight. My motto immediately became: *challenge accepted*. I am not going to *survive* cancer, I am going to *thrive!*

I was really emotional at the beginning of my treatment regime, but once all the tears were shed, I was ready to go. After my last chemo treatment, the flood of tears and excessive crying consumed me, and I felt an emotional loss. Everything is good, the treatments are done, the cancer is gone yet I was internally struggling with feelings of my whole world crashing down around me.

It took a while to really peel out of this. I think it's important to note that this is a type of grieving process. This is a step you need to go through and process to heal.

I would say my entire life movement has always helped me heal. Through any of my challenges, I've always sought out movement. After my brother's passing, which was the hardest thing to go through, even harder than my own journey, I found ballroom dancing. Dancing opened up a personal expression emotionally, physically, and spiritually.

When I was a victim of sexual assault, I found weightlifting, now a key part of my entire life. When I found out I had cancer, I found the American Ninja Warrior competition. I find myself intentionally seeking out movement or activity that is going to help me.

What I am eating definitely makes me feel a certain way. So for me, having control over what I am putting in my body, that is nourishing, nutrient dense, whole clean, natural foods, is going to affect my mood, behavior and cognition.

Feeding yourself with inflammatory foods might seem good for a moment, but that quick dopamine response doesn't feel good later, nor does it create a good relationship to your gut and brain connection. Your neurotransmitters like serotonin and dopamine are formed in your gut bacteria. So if we are feeding our microbiome healthy, nutritious, nutrient dense foods, we are feeding that bacteria in a really positive way.

During my cancer experience, I positively transformed my emotions by allowing myself to feel them. Years ago, I would have said, *"You know what, I am crying, and I really don't want to cry. I am gonna hold it in."* Now, I feel a relief to release, to cry for an entire day. I am sure it wasn't just about cancer, I'm sure it was a build up over time.

Everyone perceives me as being so strong and resilient, and all the things I have been. Just push through it and this is really hard. I don't think people understand the deeper level of this action, unless of course you have been through it yourself.

So, I think allowing myself the grace to be able to express it was a big transformative process for me. Also resorting to what always makes me feel better, which is movement, lets me take control over what I can control. Feeling physically strong has always helped me emotionally.

Four months after my cancer treatments, I competed on American Ninja Warrior. A natural progression of me starting to get back to my whatever we call normal to help me move past the strong emotional place I was sitting in. Being there, and being part of something bigger, was more than I could ever ask for.

For those of you struggling, I would say to do the things that are within your control and your power, which can be movement of any kind, paying closer attention to your nutrition and what you are putting into your body, modalities to relax, meditation … whatever resonates with you.

Staying in control of what you can do, and do the best you can, keep fighting, and just ultimately take ownership of your health. Life is always a journey regardless of a chronic illness, and just being aware of this self-control is key.

MOVEMENT AWARENESS

WHAT DID I KNOW ABOUT MOVEMENT?

Movement is just being physical. I have always been active as a child and in high school with drill team and cheerleading, and then found fitness in a gym with weights and cardio equipment. All the physical activities (sports, playing outside, riding horses and bikes, etc.) were my forms of movement. I am moving my body to sweat, lose weight, and build muscle.

WHAT DID I LEARN ABOUT MOVEMENT?

Movement, especially around emotions, is so much more. I have discovered that our emotions are energy that need to be moved through healthy modalities, so we can take it from the inside, push it away, and walk out of it. Release and let go. If we are confronted with an illness, we can cultivate our individual actions to express our feelings physically, mentally, and emotionally and fluidly communicate our needs.

CRYSTAL HEALING MOVEMENT

30 MINUTE RESTORATIVE YOGA STRETCH

A subtle place to start with this mild combination of yoga poses and stretches to release emotional tension in your body while soothing your soul.

You will need a mat, a yoga belt, bolsters, pillows or blankets for props.

Download Code Scanner on your phone or access the link on your PC. **bit.ly/3RH3BCw**

PART V
CRYSTALIZING EMOTIONAL ALCHEMY

Our emotions, when fed a balanced diet, then put into motion with natural healing mechanisms, can transform our life into a healing, breathing experience. Our existence is filled with meaning and value when we experience all the emotions.

SELF-LOVE

P ink Calcite, stimulates stagnant energy within the body; brings warmth and unwavering compassion for self and others; unconditional love for all; and is heart healing.

"I like to reference knocking my saboteur out of the way when there were things I wanted but never took the time to give myself."

— M. SAENZ, NOVEMBER 2, 2021

Mia Saenz rocks her world as a magazine editor, a co-founder and president of "Women Making Miracles," and a spiritual lover who initially self-healed her breast cancer. She has been online as a love mastery teacher and a women's empowerment transformational coach for the past 13 years.

Mia: I absolutely love and live what I do. This work is so powerful that it uplifts us into an expansive place of living. A transformational effort is done through spiritual awareness to up level yourself without fear.

I still remember the details around my cancer diagnosis phone call. And it still makes me emotional to this day. April 27, 2020, I received more of a panic call from the nurse saying I had cancer, and it's worse than we thought. Wow.

My husband and I were outside in a park near our house in the harbor on our little island in Washington State. Obviously, the vivid details are still there in the forefront of my memory.

My interpersonal development work, the self-love component, is so important because in my observation and love of research of other women, I would see their high levels of fear when confronted with a life-threatening disease (like I was), and when we believe our life is going to end in an instant, our body kicks in with an involuntary response to hyperventilation. The panic and anxiety is so intense that all of the sudden you are hyperventilating, whether you want to or not.

These actions are all attached to our emotions. Fear is the greatest emotion that can leave us frozen and in despair.

An understanding of our own self and our greatness allows us to work through all of this with a clear mind. I remember during my biopsy doing breathing techniques to stay calm. The nurse commented on my amazing mental fortitude.

As of July 22, 2020, I opted not to have surgery, and I had a conversation with God, and I began to holistically treat my body to heal. Personally, I believe loving ourselves during a cancer journey is an emotion. We gain a clarity of our own power and become empowered to easily talk ourselves out of, or down from fear, and see that it has no reality. Looking at the bigger picture, without fear, elevates our awareness and spirit into a higher vibration that will support the healing. When we are happy, negative stress isn't entering the body to actually feed disease.

Emotionally, I ate the way I needed to because it made me stay balanced. I eat a very clean diet, which is primarily vegan, and when I fall out of this regime, my body is not happy and I crave all sorts of junk. We need to think about our body as a working machine that will take care of us if we can take care of it.

I like to reference knocking my saboteur out of the way when there were things I wanted but never took the time to give myself. I started pampering myself with Epsom salt baths and all the glorious stuff in making it all about me, and talking to my body while soaking in the tub.

Self-talk is supporting everything; our body, mind and spirit. Our heart is supporting us to heal our body, mind and spirit. There is an importance around how we talk to ourselves, the demeanor in which we talk to ourselves, why we talk to ourselves.

We talk to ourselves for healing, to uplevel, and remove those spaces of negative conversation. There is a softness that is huge for healing, and plays into our emotions. We need to have these conversations with our body, head and heart.

Others have said to me, you're a love and spiritual teacher, a metaphysical practitioner, and an energy healer, why did you get cancer? So in that framework, I had to discover why the cancer came. I needed to heal in four well-being places; the emotional, mental, physical and spiritual.

Will you have a complete holistic healing like I did? Whether we choose the holistic or medical route, it doesn't matter. It is up to the individual and his/her choice. And that is what needs to be honored. So whatever choice you make, do it. Being raised in a metaphysical and holistic household, and later as a hospice nurse, I have seen patients choose death over doctors.

Look at what is right for you, and make that choice on how you want to handle that fear that will stop you from healing.

I chose to step into myself, my greater self, the warrior self, and look at my cancer, and how can I do this in a different way? I took others' research and my own, and came up with my healing protocol.

Within 5-6 months, my tumors shrunk and went dormant, which is when they declare you cancer free. This declaration doesn't give you a Free Pass GO around the board of life. We need to stay alert, aware, and continue to care about ourselves in order to have healing. This can be difficult for some, just be gentle with yourself, do what you can do, build your strength, one step at a time. Seek out support and research to become educated and informed. You don't have to do this alone.

As I teach about understanding who you are, there is a stop and an identity about how you are feeling. In general, people don't understand the feeling or emotion, they just know they don't feel right. I always ask my clients to put their hands on their chest (above the breast and below the throat) and ask: How am I feeling? How does this make me feel? Do I want more or less of it? Stopping to take in this awareness exercise pulls the emotion forward to identify and challenge it.

I always check in with myself: how am I doing? When I am upset, and can't figure a way out, I will do whatever it takes to move through it; turn on music, dance, watch a comedy, call a girlfriend to say something to make me laugh.

Nothing is more important than our health, our mindset, and our ability to shift and come back to our center. Emotions can be read, not analyzed, and reformatted back to how we want them to feel.

Arguments are shared, and when one feels shitty, and they are unaware, they put this nastiness on someone else because it makes them feel better. This emotional outlet is probably learned at a young age, and personally, coming from an abusive dysfunctional family, I have sought support and stepped up to change my emotional responses. I am taking ownership for them, and not passing the blame onto someone else, past or present.

We can always share our experience to help ease the discomforts of cancer. Always have the understanding of putting yourself first in all areas of well-being. Love yourself enough to get through this. Stop the self criticism, and try your best to be gentle and open to divine self-love.

SPOKEN

A zurite colors of deep blue, sometimes appearing black, blue, and light blue, clears away stress and worry; eases sadness and grief, brings light to emotions; increases healing abilities; and allows opening to spiritual guidance.

"Fear is dismissed with a spoken plan and a spoken place solution."

— J. MCNEES, OCTOBER 30, 2021

Jami McNees is a survivor and thriver in her bladder cancer journey. She has authored a book, *Beautiful Cancer*, has graced the TED talk stage to share her story, has created a beautiful cancer journal for purchase, and hosts a graceful podcast, "Guided Breathing for Busy Women."

Jami: I became a single mom 17 years ago when my son was 12. I am a health insurance agent, and a volunteer for Michelle's Place Cancer Resource Center. I am very active in my charity-driven community.

I have found that the matriarch of the family has championed the logistics of health insurance, so more often than not, I generally talk and work with women. At Michelle's Place, when first diagnosed, women will call in and ask for help; then they are referred to me with help in understanding insurance needs.

Leading up to my diagnosis, I remember the day of a final test to use a camera to see what was going on inside my bladder. I had no patience and used Dr. Google every day, typing in my symptoms, and every time the result was potentially bladder cancer.

Before I went in for this final test, I was in my car, music was off, and I was trying to calm myself down. In that moment, I became very aware, determined to lean in, embrace, and learn the lessons of cancer.

Whoa, Lord, what are we going to do with this? As a very avid reader, podcast listener, and lover of other self-help modalities, I sent this question into the Universe, and instantly 3 voices came back to me.

The first was Sheryl Sandberg, the CFO of Facebook, who had lost her husband, and wrote a book called, _Lean In_. Somehow her voice echoed back at me and said, "lean in." The next voice I heard was Oprah Winfrey's, and I love her Super Soul Sunday programs. She said to me, "embrace it." And the third voice I heard was Pema Chödrön. She is a little Buddhist nun with a New York accent, and her voice said to me, "everything in life is a lesson."

So, in that moment, before I even pulled into the parking lot of my doctor's office, I was determined to lean in, embrace, and learn the lessons of cancer.

A profound experience of reality. This trinity of strong influential women delivered an empowering message to help me start my healing journey.

Any cancer diagnosis, no matter how big or small, triggers, *"Oh my gosh, am I gonna die from this?"* And because it was a serious diagnosis, my brain was hijacked with fear, and just the overwhelm of the diagnosis.

My livelihood concerns kicked in as a health insurance agent. I have certain seasons where I generate 80% of my income for the year, and this diagnosis came during that time. So I needed to continue doing business, and serving people through my usual phone conversations. I found my mind constantly drifting from their needs to my own realization of *"My God, I have cancer."* I had daily challenges of focus and concentration.

As a big business book reader, strategic planning and/or sessions are a main topic of content. So, I decided, what if I have a strategic planning session with cancer, do it every day, so my mind isn't wandering for the rest of the day? So I would get ready for my work day, and before I started "work" I would go to the living room, and sit in my fancy rocking chair (my space to be with cancer.) I would speak out loud my words of fear, one being, around my chemo treatments (losing my hair), and what is the solution to this? To buy a wig. And I decided, ok, after work I am going to shop on Pinterest for amazing wigs.

Fear is dismissed with a spoken plan and a spoken place solution.

"What if this takes my life?" I took a deep breath, and said, *"What is the solution for that?"* And I realized there wasn't a solution. This was something out of my control. So the solution for me, if I couldn't control it, was released to my Creator. *"Ok, Lord, it's yours, you figure it out."*

Then I would take a deep breath, and say out loud, "Okay, I think that's it for now. I have expressed my fears, credit solutions, and I am ready to go now." Out loud, I would say, "Okay cancer, that's all the time you get today. I need you to leave me alone for the remainder of the day as I have important work to do." Then I would go to work.

I needed to be present at what I am doing, and this daily practice, I think, changed the course of my experience with cancer.

I gather nourishment from different resources. I have an Alexa in every room and ask her to play meditation or spa music to fill the room and the air with beautiful gentle sounds throughout my home. Outside my office, I have a fountain in the front yard and my kitchen window. I love the sound of water. It calms me. I also have a wind chime that has a very deep resonant bell that sounds meditative. I love when it randomly sings to me in the breeze. I have essential oils infused in my office all day long.

Another place of nourishment for me is active support at Michelle's Cancer Resource Center. When I am there, and among other cancer survivors, I feel a peace and a place for me too. Laughter is light, taking away the heaviness of cancer and all its baggage.

I have been stuck between *do I feed my body the most perfect foods* or *do I lean towards you only live once and have another taco?* And I would say during this phase, and through COVID, I was swayed to have another taco! Now the results are manifesting itself around my waistline.

So now it's time to lean back into less tacos and cookies, and find some healthier alternatives. In all honesty, I go back and forth between healthy and unhealthy food choices.

To help me optimize and move through my emotions, I intended to create a healing space to help me remain calm and less anxious. My son was 23 and living at home at the time, and for him, his emotions around his mom having cancer manifested into a negative awareness.

I could see it through his body language, I could hear it in his tone, and I could feel it through an angry fighting energy. I was working so hard to keep my environment and myself calm.

I had to have a conversation with him to explain my protection of this space, and shared, "If you can't unload your fear and anger before coming home, I will have to ask you to move out until I get through my cancer journey."

He broke down into tears, and said, "I am afraid you are going to die."

I looked at him and said, "Honey, I just have to tell you that I feel in my soul, that this cancer is not going to take my life. I am going to be here to watch you get married and have babies. I need you to recognize that my emotions, my feelings, my peacefulness is my priority at this time. So I need you to get your fear driven anger under control before you come into this house."

He started addressing his emotional place before walking through the door into mine. A few blocks from home, he would park and take deep breaths, and would arrive with a much better peaceful attitude.

I also find healing through my love of artwork that is text or graphic. I am inspired by words or quotes from movies, or song lyrics that grace many of my walls. I believe these words unconsciously fill my soul when my eyes pass them over many times a day, and become infused into my being.

In my book, _Beautiful Cancer_, I want to share how we have control over how we respond. It is the entire philosophy and research that Viktor Frankl conducted. We can't control anything around us, the only thing in our lives that we have control over is how we respond.

I see two options of difference in the people I talk to. One is going to thrive throughout this experience, and the other is going to suffer. The shared experience is the same; it is how you choose to respond: with hope, or with suffering. How do we want to respond, positively to thrive, or negatively to suffer and be miserable? Choose what ride you want to take.

Instead of getting all caught up in the external stuff that can trigger emotional overload, I chose to pack only my priorities.

My biggest nightmare is my scans showing cancer moving or growing somewhere else.

The drama, other people's problems suddenly felt petty to me, and even today, eight years out, this still rings true for me. The political climate, the arguing, the ostracizing of others, etc., on social media and beyond, is so petty. Why are you wasting time on this?

Their priorities are screwed up. I will be there for them when the universe says, *okay, it's time to learn what's important and what's not.* And, see how that manifests itself, and then support them through that, Right?

Personally, I shared my diagnosis with family and close friends, and then struggled on where to go from there with my experience with bladder cancer. Do I continue to keep it on the down low, and stay with my current shared community?

When a colleague reached out and shared her knowledge of my cancer, I had questions of what to do with this knowledge. Who do I tell? Why do I tell? She responded that people who tried to go through cancer alone are more likely to suffer from PTSD later on. And I didn't want to add PTSD into my illness mix.

I chose to put it out into the world on Facebook. This is what I have, this is my plan to handle it, and I used positive words to show strength and beauty around my healing. My FB community responded with love, support, healing prayers, and positive vibes. How can I not come out of this?

So, I would advise someone going through the same experience or who has just been diagnosed, to share. Let others know what you are going through so that they have the opportunity to send love and support.

BALANCE

Clear Quartz, colorless and transparent, balances and revitalizes the physical, mental, emotional, and spiritual planes; stimulates the immune system; and brings the body into balance.

"When you link the affirmation with the particular emotion associated with a particular experience, it moves to another level of understanding to shift it to the positive polarity, as opposed to being stuck in the negative pulvinar."

— DR. C. MEIN, DECEMBER 1, 2021

Dr. Carolyn Mein is a nationally recognized author, speaker and expert on health and nutrition. She holds degrees in chiropractic, acupuncture, applied nutrition and bio nutrition, and has a long standing private practice in California.

Carolyn: My background is primarily in chiropractic acupuncture in nutrition. And my beginning practice started with applied kinesiology where I started asking the body various questions, and found muscle testing a very effective tool to gain valuable information regarding a client's health.

My work and research has gained depth over the years with acupuncture, stabilization of the bodily system, and cranial structure corrections. The chiropractic premise is that the central nervous system controls and regulates everything. And in making sure all the systems work together, my focus has been primarily on the structural and dietary areas. A blanket diet for all does not feed individual system appetites. There was a need to go into more specifics to find what foods would really support the system.

In looking at different body types, and their emotional components, I found that there are personality profiles with each particular body type that goes into what motivates you. Your passion, food and personality areas are not the same as everyone else. I started looking at essential oils as a way to shift a negative emotion to a positive one, and have authored a book on releasing emotional patterns with essential oils.[1]

Most of us are familiar with the negative side of an emotion, and the positive side is vague and unclear. The challenge is why did I create this emotion, and what do I need to do in order to move out of it?

My pursuit in health, wellness, and nutrition started with chiropractic care which has been a mainstay in my life since I was an infant, and later, I ended up working for a chiropractor and found that this was something that really resonated with me. This work experience led to school to learn and eventually practice as a doctor of chiropractic care.

My father died of cancer at 45, right after my graduation from chiropractic college. His untimely passing and just finishing school led me in the direction of looking at diet, nutrition, health, and healing from multiple perspectives, to be able to see what is really going to make a difference.

I wanted to explain a little bit about transpersonal physiology, and how it can help with emotions related to chronic illness.

Transpersonal physiology is a combination technique of chiropractic and acupuncture that uses a code to set up a vibrational frequency done on the sternum. This frequency, as a diagnostic tool, is being used to access different parts of the body. Then traditional acupuncture points are used to connect the energy circuit.

The third component of transpersonal physiology is the nutrition/dietary area, where I discovered the 25 body types, and how they work with applied kinesiology, individual supplementation, and other pertinent combinations.

My interest in body systems and types began with doctoral research around the three strongest glands: the adrenal, the pituitary, and the thyroid. Another physician and diet counselor, Dr. Elliot Abravanel, used these three types in his book, _Body Type and Nutrition Plan_, introducing another gland present in women (gonadal), and notably not in men.

This piqued my interest and my work around discovering that yes, men do have a gonadal gland. Further research led to not only dominant gland types, but organs and systems as well equaling 25 different body types. Body type is genetic, and is based upon your dominant gland organ or system to result in individual weight gain, food cravings, energy levels, etc., and for some people more than others, what times of the day to consume certain foods and/or your micronutrients.

Essential oils support nourishment and play a part in healing through a positive frequency. And the lack of research around how we access emotions through the limbic system of the brain. And that's access to your smell. Smell, in comparison to our emotional processing through our other senses, has been neglected, and is very important to our emotional well-being. Working with essential oils and the acupuncture alarm point, you could access where that emotion was held in the body.

Traditional acupuncture proves that emotions are held in different places of the body, so how do we access them, and deal with them? In looking at cancer and as a personal cure of a fatal disease, Norman Cousins, *Anatomy of an Illness*, discovered the common denominator is an illiterate component, and the emotion stored in the liver is anger. So to transmute the anger held in the liver and reverse the profile, he resorted to the opposite of anger which is laughter. His consumption of funny movies brought much laughter and a reversal to the whole profile.

Cancer is a place of self-denial. There is a tendency to think I am strong, and I can handle it. This is an internalization of emotion. You should look at that emotion, how to deal with it, transmute it, and shift it. Again, on the negative side of emotions, if you don't know what it is, how are you going to access it? And on the positive side, why did you create it, which is where affirmations come in. I have found affirmations to be really valuable.

When you link the affirmation with the particular emotion associated with a particular experience, it moves to another level of understanding to shift it to the positive polarity, as opposed to being stuck in the negative pulvinar.

I personally optimize my emotions through first identifying what it is. Really looking at what is there. Then what is on the other side of that? What do I need to learn from this experience, and when I need to gain from it?

Then I bring my essential oils in to identify a positive frequency. When you find yourself in the negative polarity, or the negative emotion, the positive may appear as a thought, a concept. What you do to bring that into your body and into a cellular resonance is supported through essential oils because they will hold the frequency and allow you to bridge the gap and get to that particular place of positive emotion.

The specific emotion essential oil would be applied to where the emotion is held in the body. So for example, if the emotion is anger, you would apply the oil using the liver acupuncture point on the hands or the feet. You are accessing where that energy is held in your body. Other personal favorite points for emotional release are the forehead; above the eyes or at the hairline (stress); the top of the head (crown chakra spiritual connection); and the back of the head at the base of the skull.

We also have two other depressed points on the back of the head, on the occipital area, that are filters to release other people's emotional stuff you may be picking up creating a feeling of being stuck. Smelling the oil that connects with the limbic system of the brain, connects with the emotion of using anger, and then a direct connection with anger. What does it feel like? Where is it showing up in your life? Where is it stored in your body, and using deep breathing to let it go.

Then on the other side of anger is laughter. Taking a breath in to breath in laughter and connecting with what laughter feels like. Where is it, if you don't feel like laughing? Think of a time when you did laugh, or something that would make you laugh. Or the thought of bringing laughter into the areas where the anger was held, breathing out, and letting that go in the same place with the body. And the affirmation brings clarity on how you get from anger to laughter.

What is causing the anger? It is a lot like a traffic jam. Traffic is moving, energy flowing, all is good, then you hit a roadblock. When you hit a roadblock, energy builds until you finally get to the point of exploding, an explosion of negative energy, and an explosion of positive energy, there is laughter. This is when you see the difference, and how on the other side of anger is laughter, and you are able to transmute it.

So how do you do this? Going back to the traffic jam example, you find yourself in a roadblock or jam, so you would turn on the radio.

The radio access is the traffic helicopter who is able to see things from a higher perspective, which is what you do in meditation.

This is where the affirmation comes in. Your affirmation is affirming the positive answer to the problem. And so the question is, I am in this mess, what do I do? You say your affirmation, my direction is clear, and this allows a let go of anger to experience laughter.

The polarity of emotional processing with essential oils and affirmations is very empowering.

To apply, take a drop on your non-dominant hand, rotate clockwise three times to wake it up, to stimulate the oil, then take the oil to dab on the acupuncture points for the particular emotion, breathing in the scent, feeling and connecting with the emotions. Certain oils go with certain moods or emotions. You can access this correlation on your computer or download an app on your phone. Go to www.bodytype.com/oils/ to move through the whole process.

Some healthy recommended nuggets of advice to transform your emotions would be to look into things that are going on with you. A self-evaluation of your current health, diet, nutrition, lifestyle, and your status of emotional health. This check-in will allow you to see what is really going on, and help you decide what you need to do to bring your system back into balance. And the message you receive from this experience will grant you the power to change it.

TRANSFORM

Tiger's Eye Quartz, is a brownish yellow or brown in its natural state, that heals issues of self-worth and self-criticism; associates with abundance, optimism, and manifestation; and is helpful in recognizing one's own needs in relation to the needs of others.

> "I absolutely believe that emotions play into what shows up in our body, whether it's good or bad, in between, whatever, and I do believe that unresolved emotions, and unresolved or unhealed trauma, is the root or the basis of where disease in our body comes from."

— E.L. WILSON, DECEMBER 21, 2021

Emily Louise Wilson is an elite online health, fitness coach and plant-based diva.

Emily: I grew up as an active athlete, and continued moving to cultivate a personal and professional lifestyle around health and fitness. My education in kinesiology, with an emphasis in exercise science, extensive yoga study, a certification in precision nutrition, CrossFit, and weightlifting have helped me craft my coaching business for over 10 years now.

In the past three years, I have gotten more into inner work, the emotional work to complement my client's external fix of health that consisted mainly of meal and exercise plans. I was finding that putting together these plans might get clients to a certain place in their health and fitness journey, but there always seems to be a barrier that stops them from making a full integration.

It really has to do with the stories we tell ourselves, our identity, that we have around our bodies, and our relationship to food. Creating health and fitness is truly an inside out job. My focus has shifted toward supporting people to create their ultimate health plan for life and not just a quick fix.

I truly believe that things accumulate, and when we are not always ready to make a change, until suddenly, it clicks. And then it's time. When I chose to go vegan, I was listening to an interview between Rich Roll, an incredible plant-based endurance athlete, and James Aspey, a vegan activist from Australia.

I was hearing him describe the reality of the dairy industry. At that moment, I was eating milk chocolate chips! And as he's describing what goes on in that industry, I literally felt a visceral dusting. And in that moment, things clicked for me, I realized I didn't want to contribute to that system. Because it's inherently violent, and causes a lot of suffering. I pushed the chocolate away, and swore I would never eat that stuff again. It was that quick for me.

Before this revelation, I had been exposed to veganism throughout my life, and I've opened up magazine articles and read things about speciesism, and things like that. And at that time, I wasn't ready to take it in.

So, for me, the years of accumulated information and exposure to things around veganism and animal rights, finally clicked for me, I was ready to make a change.

I have been fortunate in not having any chronic illnesses. I will say though, before I transitioned to being vegan, I was vegetarian. There have been moments in my life where I have tried to incorporate meat and other animal products, and it just does not work for me.

So, as a vegetarian, I was consuming a lot of dairy products, and all tasted really good; however, after transitioning, and not noticing a huge change in my body, I did over time, feel a level of mental clarity, almost like a fog lifted. This feeling brought a spatial openness to my body and my heart, and eventually lifted an annoying low grade stomach ache which I didn't know existed until going off dairy.

I absolutely believe that emotions play into what shows up in our body, whether it's good or bad, in between, whatever, and I do believe that unresolved emotions, and unresolved or unhealed trauma, is the root or the basis of where disease in our body comes from.

Personally, I experience occasional back pain which initially started from years of stress and strain on my body from gymnastics, and lack of proper training. This pain is still manifested in my body, and I really feel it when I am experiencing stress and anxiety, not from physical activity, but from an internal struggle. My fight or flight response is turned on, and I am in a heightened state of constant pain where I can't do anything.

I have experienced long-term back pain and now know it comes from trapped emotion(s). My physical ailments are directly related to my internal struggles. Some other emotional feelings that I can share are related to my experience with lockjaw where I couldn't open my mouth fully. These pains and restrictions were not from anything physical, but from my emotional ignorance. I wasn't being honest with myself and how I was feeling. And I wasn't being honest with the people in my life, and what was going on in our dynamic.

I am basically not living in my reality. I am lying, hiding, concealing, and masking in order to make things OK. Living here is not fair to me or to those I have relationships with. And so, hiding in this dishonesty, I wasn't speaking up, I wasn't using my voice which caused my jaw to lock up.

And when the back pain appears, I have noticed, is when I am not being fully transparent and honest. I am basically stuffing whatever the emotion is; fear, anger, hurt, sadness. I am just keeping it inside, and not expressing it.

I notice differences and contrasts when I eat high quality whole plant-based foods versus low quality, highly processed foods. I can feel it in my body with a tightness, in my head with a fogginess, creating a lack of clarity. I notice my mood and emotions when I am eating less clean, are sluggish and I question my existence and priorities. I feel less capable to show up, live my life, be happy, and be available for others.

So, if I am not prioritizing my eating well, it really brings me down. And when I do eat well, without thinking about it, I show up as myself and tap into the truth of who I am. I am being, and it's just happening, and it feels great!

Being raised in Idaho around hunting and raising sheep for meat, I, from a very early age, just didn't appreciate meat or the taste of it. I would substitute my protein from highly processed foods like hot dogs or deli sliced meat, anything that didn't look or taste like an animal.

My emotional transformation has come from many modalities. I have completed different things like inner child work, integrations, and shadow work to help me. Allowing myself to feel what I feel, and not judge it. Not make myself wrong for it, and not take it out on other people. When I am having strong negative emotional reactions, having the awareness, going inward and asking with curiosity, *"I am feeling angry right now." "That's fine. I get to feel this anger." "What?" "Why are you feeling angry, what's going on here?"*

Literally being with my emotions, and whatever comes up, crying, making noise, journaling, just allowing it to be okay to feel, because I have noticed that when I allow it, allow myself to feel it, it usually passes through quite quickly. Whereas, it's when I resist and block it, I am like, I shouldn't feel this. When I need to feel this way, instead of this way, then the emotion continues with persistence and it doesn't clear out.

I need to feel it, be with myself, in a safe space for that tough emotion to exist.

While we are talking about alchemizing our emotions, getting to the root cause of whatever it is we are experiencing, disease or otherwise, we are creating the health, fitness, or life we want in any area of our life.

Movement is medicine. We need to prioritize this bodily attribute to stay active through dancing, walking, lifting weights, etc. to accommodate our aging process. If we are not moving our bodies, eventually, they are not going to move for us. Movement helps us work through our emotions, creating a flow to release things that are energetically stuck.

Many of us have inner dialogues that go on in our head, and oftentimes they're negative, especially if they relate to your body, your health, your relationship with food. Stay curious and question them, and don't take them as truth. Notice it, become aware of it, and then question it, "Is that even true?" When we take this negative dialogue as truth, we live from that identity.

Choose a new story and a new belief that aligns with what you want to create in your health, life, and/or relationships.

EMOTIONAL ALCHEMY AWARENESS

WHAT DID I KNOW ABOUT EMOTIONAL ALCHEMY?

What is emotional alchemy? My prior research and personal work up to this point solidified my breast cancer diagnosis as years of manifesting emotional imbalances. My continual search for external happiness, affirmation, and acknowledgment was an unintentional and unlearned ignorance to not loving myself and realizing my happiness is within.

My former self remained silent, fuming, anger bubbling, reacting, to conform, and blend in without confrontation. To then sometimes blow up after so much time not making any sense of my former upset or anger.

WHAT DID I LEARN ABOUT EMOTIONAL ALCHEMY?

Now I understand and practice the necessity to love me, to hold inner dialogues of curiosity and questions for my emotions. To stay disease-free and present, I need to get to the root of my emotion to accentuate my health and healing for life. I own my emotions, I get to observe, challenge and change them to help me, and to help others.

Take away the diseased reaction to create a healthy action.

CRYSTAL HEALING MEDITATION

EMOTIONAL AWARENESS RELAXATION MEDITATION

Find a comfortable, quiet place to sit or lie down. Close your eyes, relax your face, and begin breathing in and out through your nose. Start with this box breath cycle.

Deep inhalation through the nose for 4 counts
Hold for 4 counts
Exhale from the nose for 4 counts
Hold for 4 counts
Repeat this cyclic breathing 2 to 3 times before you begin the meditation.
Then follow along, really taking in all this meditation is offering you. Repeat as many times as you need.

Download Code Scanner on your phone or access the link on your PC. **bit.ly/3Xh143b**

CONCLUSION

My health is a crystal forming, alchemizing, in my relationship to three healing pillars; nourishment, movement, and emotional alchemy. I wanted to weave a theme around crystals and their healing energy, how they are formed through crystallization to support a transformation from the chaos of chronic illness to a personal place of health and vitality.

Discovering breast cancer is like uncovering a new crystal buried deep inside the earth, with an appearance that will depend upon its natural features and the conditions in which it grows. Cancer can hold strange shapes, and sizes, depending on its manifesting timeline. Mine appeared as a smooth moving gem under my right armpit, fast-tracking my lymph system on its way to other origins of illness.

Just like a crystal, my negative emotional energies need a cleansing, a positive connection, in order to promote my own healing. As I focus on nourishing all facets of my well-being, I am aware of my available choices to intentionally support a balance of health and healing.

My cancer experience birthed a new reality around emotional awareness and choices. My places of well-being have less intensity and more ease and flow to manifest and make decisions that nourish me in a healthier way.

As I continue nurturing my emotional processes, I strive to transmute holistic practices as a path towards living my most enriched life. My crystal healing journey flows from a place of illness to one of habitual health. This path and growth are fed by nourishing my emotions with better food choices, continued physical activity, mental awareness practices, social cleansing, and spiritual enlightenment.

I think most of us go through the motions and do what we have to do. We listen to the person with authority to tell us what to do without any self-thought or verbal conversation around personal fears, and how to move through them. My story and those of others hold a space for healing by allowing our positive, abundant energy to flow into you, the reader, to help take away the negative toxic energy of emotional suffering.

As this healing process is what aligned and worked for me, which may not work for you, my sincere hope is to provide an understanding around pursuing alternative choices to live your most abundant life, to thrive.

THANKS SO MUCH!

For honoring your gravitational pull towards my collaborative conversation to support your emotional healing.

My hope is to bring healthy awareness with possible choices to those of you struggling, surviving, or care-taking of another, to thrive despite a chronic illness.

And, in thinking of friends and loved ones who may benefit from this energetic guidance, please share. Here are some ways to do this.

Stay connected on social media, follow and tag me here: **www.linktr.ee/crystalg03**

Sometimes it is frustrating and fearful to do it alone. I want to be your guide as we walk together on a path towards emotional health and healing vitality. I invite a heart-felt connection here:

info@crystalgrenier.com

If you have found this book useful we request you take 60 seconds to leave an honest review on **Amazon** amzn.to/3kEYDuc and/or **Goodreads.com .**

In Gratitude,

ABOUT THE AUTHOR

Image by SP Photography

Crystal D. Grenier is a breast cancer survivor who offers heart-felt guidance in all facets of illness to reclaim your health and restore your vitality using natural modalities.

Her deep background in health and fitness, as well as her cancer experience, have given her the tools to share intentional insight into alternative methods of self-acceptance, continued growth, and abundant living. An active yogi, she has created, implemented and participated in numerous health and wellness retreats.

Crystal is a contributing writer for Thrive Global, a local newspaper column, "Healing through Conversation," and a contributing author in *Feisty: Dangerously Amazing Women Using Their Voices & Making an Impact.*

She holds a Bachelors in Communications/Business and a Masters in Sports Management. She currently lives in North Dakota, and is married with two adult daughters.

Crystal is an online wellness consultant who helps women thrive despite a chronic illness through guided offers around emotional health focusing on her healing pillars of support: nourishment, movement and alchemy.

www.linktr.ee/crystalg03

ALSO BY CRYSTAL D. GRENIER

www.amazon.com/author/crystaldgrenier

COLLABORATIVE AUTHOR BOOKS

Feisty: Dangerously Amazing Women Using Their Voices & Making an Impact

RED THREAD BOOKS

Red Thread Publishing is an all-female publishing company on a mission to support 10,000 women to become successful published authorpreneurs & thought leaders.

To work with us or connect regarding any of our growing library of books email us at **info@redthreadbooks.com.**

To learn more bout us visit our website

www.redthreadbooks.com.

Follow us & join the community.

facebook.com/redthreadpublishing

instagram.com/redthreadbooks

SOURCES

Abravanel MD, E.D., & King, E.A. (1999). *Dr. Abravanel's Body Type Diet and Lifetime Nutrition Plan.* Revised. Random House Publishing Group.

Anamarie, Content Pixie. (2021). *White Envelope on Black Table.* https://unsplash.com/photos/h_Mn2zJMWQY

Caryl. (2023). Rose Quartz Healing Properties. https://www.charmsoflight.com/rose-quartz-healing-properties

Cousins, N. (2005). *Anatomy of an Illness: As Perceived by the Patient.* W.W. Norton & Company.

Coyote T. (2021). Grace, Grit & Gratitude: *A Cancer Thriver's Journey from Hospice to Full Recovery with the Healing Power of Horses.* Self-Published.

Coyote, Tara. Interview. Conducted by Crystal Grenier. 02 Nov 2021.

Dendy, Talaya. Interview. Conducted by Crystal Grenier. 07 Dec 2021.

Dimas, J. (2022, November 11). 50 Journal Prompts for Clarity, Well-Being, & Healing. https://jessicadimas.com/journal-prompts-clarity-well-being-healing/

Elizabeth, D. (2022, June 21). 18 Ways to Intentionally Nurture and Nourish Your Soul. https://wildsimplejoy.com/how-to-nourish-your-soul-meaning/

Ellis, T. (2023). *Book Cover, Crystalize Your Health, Crystal Images.* www.linktr.ee/Tarnellisart

Emma. (2023). Crystals & Stones for Nourishment. https://crystal-curious.com/use/nourishment/

Ertel, LCSW, BCD, A. (2021, November 19). Your Guide to Understanding Emotional Health. https://www.talkspace.com/blog/emotional-health-definition/

Ewers, Dr. Keesha. Interview. Conducted by Crystal Grenier. 18 Nov 2021.

Green, Tamara. Interview. Conducted by Crystal Grenier. 08 Dec 2021.

Green, T. & Grossman, S. (2021). *The Living Kitchen: Nourishing Whole-Food Recipes for Cancer Treatment and Recovery.* Appetite by Random House.

Grenier, C. (2022). A Recipe for Alchemizing Our Emotions to Heal. Red Thread Publishing LLC. *FEISTY: Dangerously Amazing Women Using Their Voices & Making An Impact (Brave New Voices).* (pp. 141-150).

Hamilton PhD, D.R. (2021). Crystals. *Why Woo Woo Works. The Surprising Science Behind Meditation. Reiki, Crystals, and Other Alternative Practices.* 1st Edition. Hay House. (pp. 117-148).

Harrison, M. (2023). 12 Crystals for Energy: Access Invigorating Energy & Drive. https://cosmiccuts.com/blogs/healing-stones-blog/crystals-for-energy

Hellman, R. (2019, December 9). To Thrive, Get a Balanced Diet of Social Nutrition. https://today.ku.edu/2019/12/04/thrive-get-balanced-diet-social-nutrition

https://raskrasil.com/en/crystal-coloring-pages

JuliaDreamsCo. (2023). *Watercolor Crystals and Gemstones Clipart Set from Encyclopedia of Astrology Collection.* https://www.etsy.com/listing/927704

914/watercolor-crystals-and-gemstones

Korth, Christie. Interview. Conducted by Crystal Grenier. 20 Dec 2021.

Lakhi, Priya. Interview. Conducted by Crystal Grenier. 19 Nov 2021.

McNees, J. (2017). *Beautiful Cancer.*

McNees, Jami. Interview. Conducted by Crystal Grenier. 30 Oct 2021.

Mein, Dr. Carolyn. Interview. Conducted by Crystal Grenier. 01 Dec 2021.

Mein, Carolyn L. (2020). *Releasing Patterns With Essential Oils.* VisionWare Press.

Missimer, Arianne. Interview. Conducted by Crystal Grenier. 08 Dec 2021.

Montry, Lori. Interview. Conducted by Crystal Grenier. 16 Dec 2021.

Natalie, IPurpleMoon. (2023). *23 Gemstones.* https://www.etsy.com/listing/1311099363/watercolor-crystals-clipart-gemstones.

Saenz, Mia. Interview. Conducted by Crystal Grenier. 02 Nov 2021.

Shannon, Marie. (2023). Pink Calcite Spiritual Properties: Stone of Compassion. https://crystal-wisdom.com/2021/09/24/pink-calcite-spiritual-properties-stone-of-compassion/

Stone Mania Crystals Rocks Minerals. (2023). Articles and Photos. ttps://www.stonemania.co.uk/crystals/

Wilson, Emily Louise. Interview. Conducted by Crystal Grenier. 21 Dec 2021.

Yates, Brad. Interview. Conducted by Crystal Grenier. 29 Nov 2021.

NOTES

4. HEART-FELT CONNECTIONS

1. Two of the interviewees opted out of my book due to their new direction and business branding.

11. FLOWING FORGIVENESS

1. Tara's paternal family originates from Hawaii.

20. BALANCE

1. Mein, Carolyn L. *Releasing Patterns With Essential Oils* (VisionWare Press, 2020) https://www.amazon.com/Releasing-Emotional-Patterns-Essential-Oils/dp/0966138198

Made in the USA
Monee, IL
15 October 2023

44599533R00080